NATIVE AMERICAN

LEGENDS
and
ACTIVITIES

by

Mari Lu Robbins

SCHOLASTIC
PROFESSIONAL BOOKS

NEW YORK • TORONTO • LONDON • AUCKLAND • SYDNEY

TABLE OF CONTENTS

INTRODUCTION 4

STORIES FROM THE EASTERN WOODLANDS 12

Great Turtle Makes the World 17

The Broken Wing 20

Lone Bird, the Woman in the Moon 23

Little People of the Micmac 27

The Origin of Corn 29

Origin of the Pleiades 31

How Deer Got His Horns 33

STORIES FROM THE GREAT PLAINS 36

Old Man Teaches the People 39

White Buffalo Woman 42

The Boy and the Turtles 45

STORIES FROM THE SOUTHWEST 48

Coyote and the Woodpeckers 52

The Mother Moon 55

Turkey Makes Corn and Coyote Plants It 57

The Coyote and the Bear 60

STORIES FROM THE FAR WEST 63

Origin of the Sierra Nevada and the Coast Range 68

Coyote Makes First Man 70

How Robin Got His Red Breast 73

STORIES FROM THE NORTHWEST 75

Pushing Up the Sky 81

Wakiash and the First Totem Pole 84

The Great Canoe in the Sky 88

The Animals Climb into the Sky 90

The Origin of Cedar Trees 93

The Punishment of the Stingy 95

INTRODUCTION

It is said that people need stories as much as they need food and water. The stories give people what they need to know in order to live together harmoniously and tell them why they are here and how they got here. The stories carry down the beliefs and traditions of the people from one generation to the next.

The original residents of North America came at least 30 to 40 thousand years ago. There are many names used to describe these people. In this book we refer to them as Native Americans. The Native Americans had many names for themselves. When translated into English many of these names meant "The People," as this is what they called themselves.

This book contains legends of the Native Americans. A *legend* is a story that has been passed down from generation to generation. The legends are set in the historical past or in the present. They are a mixture of fact and fiction and were regarded by the Native Americans as being truth. Legends generally represent the attitudes and values of a group. The legends here are mostly about the origin of the world, people, and items, or else they impart a moral or religious lesson. Some legends are purely for entertainment. Most of these legends take place in a time when the earth was young and not as it is now. In most cases animals were the original inhabitants. The animals were seen as being just like human beings. Originally, legends were passed down orally as Native Americans did not begin to write until Sequoyah invented the alphabet for the Cherokee in 1820.

The Native Americans have always believed the earth is sacred because it was given to them by the Creator. The Creator takes many forms and varies from legend to legend. Sometimes the Creator is an animal, as in some California and Northwest legends where the Coyote is the Creator. Sometimes the legend simply says the Creator. But the Creator is considered to be the source of all life. The Native Americans believe that every animal, plant, stone, and heavenly body has a spirit of its own, very much like their own. By respecting and honoring the spirits, the Native Americans thought their lives would be peaceful.

Native American legends include animals as well as people. The animals have the same characteristics as people; they can talk and think as we do. In many legends animals play the same part over and over again. For example, in the Southwest and California, the Coyote plays the part of a trickster. Generally, whenever the Coyote appears in one of these legends, he is almost always the trickster of the story. In the Northwest, Bluejay is the trickster, and in the Woodlands the trickster is Rabbit.

The traditional time for telling stories was after the sun went down on long winter evenings when the family was gathered around the fire. Stories were not usually told during the day or in the summer because then the animals were about, and their feelings would be hurt if they heard themselves being discussed. Children were expected to learn the stories from memory so that they could pass them on to their own children. Stories were considered part of their education.

As you read these legends, you will find that stories from one region are very similar to stories from another region or another group in the region. Such is the case when dealing with the origin of the earth. The Iroquois legend *Great Turtle Makes the World* is retold in many parts of the East Coast using different animals, but the results are always the same. Little people appear in stories from different regions, such as the Micmac story *Little People of the Micmac* and the Sioux story *The Boy and the Turtles*. Some stories were creation stories, telling how the world and its

inhabitants began in a distant myth-making time when animals and people talked with each other, and the stars still lived on earth. Such is the case in *Lone Bird, The Woman in the Moon* from the Chippewa people, *The Mother Moon* from the Pueblos, and *The Great Canoe in the Sky* from the Salish. Some stories teach what can happen to someone who does something wrong, as in the Chinook story *The Punishment of the Stingy*; some teach how fire came to be.

Whatever the theme of the story, the lessons are universal and apply, in most cases, to the lives of people today. As students read these legends, they will be able to identify the values and beliefs that were important to each group. Reading these legends may help students relate to other peoples and other times in a positive manner.

TEACHING ACROSS THE CURRICULUM

Native American myths and legends are ideal for teaching across the curriculum. The stories can be used to evoke student interest in science, social studies, language arts, and the fine arts by helping them compare and contrast ideas presented in the stories with modern knowledge.

Try using some of the following suggestions for discussion topics and activities when teaching across the curriculum.

SOCIAL STUDIES

1 Discuss the geographical settings of the stories. For example, if place names are mentioned in a legend, have students look them up on a map. Have students think about the foods found in an area. Discuss how the available foods might affect the stories. How might the stories of people who eat mostly fish be different from the stories told by the buffalo hunters or farmers? Discuss the values that would be common to people of many diverse geographical locations.

2 Discuss what the beliefs of the people in the story are. Have students determine what was important to the people. Compare these beliefs from region to region. Which are similar? Which are different?

3 Have students research the culture of one of the Native American groups represented in these legends. They could find out about the area they lived in, the types of homes they had, the role of the men and women, what children were taught, and so on.

4 Students can research the types of housing such as the long houses, tipi, and pueblo used by various groups. Then have them construct little models of each type.

LANGUAGE ARTS

1 When these stories were told a hundred or more years ago, the storyteller also used body language. A story was acted out by the storyteller, and sound effects might have been used, such as the pounding of the hooves of many horses, or the whooshing of the wind. Have students learn a story by heart. Then have them tell the story to the class using body language and sound effects to show what is happening in the story.

2 Tell one of the stories with the use of aids, such as puppets, shadowplays, or masks.

3 Have students write a paper on the moral, or lesson, of a story. They should identify how they could tell what the moral is.

4 Have students rewrite one of the stories, retelling it in a modern setting or just changing the outcome of the story.

5 Students can rewrite a story as a play or an animated film.

6 Discuss how a story is similar to or different from another one they have read.

7 Have students write newspaper headlines and/or a story that represents one of the legends. Explain the who, what, when, where, and why of journalism writing.

SCIENCE

1 In the past, people have used stories to explain certain aspects of life that were frightening or confusing, such as illnesses and natural phenomena like earthquakes, floods, and lightning. How would modern science tend to take the place of stories in this respect?

2 Many stories give mythical explanations of how things came to be, such as how fire came to be, what happened to the buffalo on the Plains, and how the Sierra Nevada and Coast Range came to be. Have students find out the scientific reasons for these things.

ART

1 Bring books to class that contain pictures of Native American art.

Discuss how the stories a people tell affect the kinds of artistic expression they engage in.

2 Discuss the relationship between the geography of a people and the arts they produce.

3 If you have any students interested in acting, you may wish to have them act out one of the legends in the book or have a dramatic reading of the legend. Have interested students group themselves according to the legend they want to enact. Working together, have them decide on how they will perform the legend, such as adding sound effects, doing scenery, and so on. Some legends may have to be altered slightly to work in the classroom.

4 When reading these stories, have students note the pictures that come to mind. Using various materials, have students put those pictures on paper.

5 Dance was an integral part of the Native American culture. Some dances took place to ensure good rainfall or a bountiful harvest. Some were to celebrate a victory, or just for fun. Have students research, and, if you wish, perform some Native American dances.

How to Read These Stories

A varied approach to reading the stories in this book will help more of your students to understand and appreciate them. Each person learns in a slightly different way. Some people are visual; they learn best by seeing something. Some people are auditory; they learn best by hearing. Others are kinetic; they learn best by using their bodies and their senses.

Most people learn by a combination of all these different modalities. The more varied the activities are, the more successful the learning will be. Many classrooms today contain students with widely varying needs. Some students may be visually impaired or hearing impaired or have learning disabilities. Using a wide variety of teaching methods will help all students be successful. The following suggested activities can be done before or after the story is read.

* Before reading the stories, determine what your students know about the Native Americans of North America. Discuss the fact that until a century ago, most of the people who first told these stories had a much closer relationship with nature than most of us have today, because their very lives depended on working with nature for their food, shelter, and other basic necessities of life. Discuss how storms, droughts, and other natural phenomena may have been different for them than for people today who live in houses or apartment buildings.

* Before, during, and after reading these stories, discuss stories students have read or heard that were told by peoples in other parts of the world, such as Greek and Roman myths or European or Asian folk tales. How might they be different? How might they be similar?

* Compile a class vocabulary book in which students record words from the stories that are new to them along with their definitions. An effective way of doing this is to use a chart-paper tablet on a tripod at the front of the room. Words can be discussed and used in context in new sentences to reinforce learning.

* After having the students read a story silently to familiarize themselves with it, ask them to read the story aloud paying close attention to expression.

* Give the students a paragraph from a story in which some of the words have been left out, and have them fill in the correct words.

* Have students compile their own story books by rewriting and

illustrating the stories in a composition book.

✳ Discuss the "before and after" of a story. How was the character at the beginning? How did he/she change as a result of what happened?

✳ Learn one of the arts and crafts practiced by the people who told this story and make your own version of it. Or, have an expert come in and demonstrate something like basket weaving or wood carving, or perhaps make a special food.

✳ Discuss with students what the effect would be if a certain character (name one) had done something differently than he or she did. Would the story have another ending? Would the character have changed in the same way with this ending?

✳ Have students write a paragraph or a page telling how two or three stories are like each other. Then have them write another paragraph or page telling how those same stories are different from each other.

✳ Have students categorize the stories by the headings Creation, Heavenly Bodies, Teaching, Morals, and Entertainment. Have students write an explanation for their choices.

✳ Have students identify the main idea of a story. Then have them write a paragraph telling how the main idea is apparent and another paragraph telling what facts or events in the story support this main idea.

✳ Have students identify which of the characters in a story, or stories, was their favorite. Then have them write a paragraph explaining why they chose that character.

✳ Discuss how students would change a story. To get them started, ask: What is one way in which the main character of the story could have acted differently? What do you think would have been the likely result if he or she had acted that way? Then have students rewrite the story with their changes. Discuss how their changes may have affected the ending of the story or the moral.

✳ Have students visualize themselves in the story. Have them rewrite the story having one character solve his or her problem in a different way than he/she did. Discuss what students would have done in his or her place.

✳ Have students write a story with the same topic and characters as in this story, but change the setting to one with which they are familiar in their own lives.

Pronunciation Guide for use with the stories in this book

Abenaki (AHB-uh-nah-kee)

Apache (ah-PATCH-ee)

Anit'sutsa (A NIT soot-sah)

Cherokee (CHAIR-o-kee)

Chinook (shi-NOOK)

Chippewa (CHIP-uh-wah)

Coyote (ky-YO-tee) or (ky-YOHT)

Haida (HAY-duh)

Hopi (HO-pee)

Iroquois (EAR-uh-koy)

Kareya (kuh-RAY-uh)

Karok (KAIR-uk)

Kootenay (KOOT-nay)

Kwakiutl (KWAH-kee-eu-tul)

Micmac (MIK-mak)

Miwok or Mewok (MEE-wok)

Okanagon (Oh-KAN-uh-gun)

Pleiades (PLEE-uh-dees)

Pueblo (PWEB-loh)

Puget (PEU-jet)

Salish (SAY-lish)

Sierra Nevada (see-AIR-uh nuh-VAD-uh)

Sioux (SOO)

Snohomish (snoh-HOH-mish)

Tulare (too-LAIR-ee)

Wakiash (WAH-kee-ahsh)

Yokuts (YOH-cuts)

HOW THIS BOOK IS ORGANIZED

The stories in this book are arranged according to the five roughly geographical areas from which they come: Eastern Woodlands, Great Plains, Southwest, Far West, and Northwest. Because of space limitations, it is impossible to really do justice to all the Native American groups. There are so many stories and groups that many have been left out. There is no intention to slight any groups; using five geographical areas is simply a rough way of organizing the stories.

Each section begins with a brief introduction about the geographic group and is followed by a brief synopsis of each legend. (You may wish to share some of this information with your students before they read the legend.) Following the synopsis are an assortment of cross-curricular activities that pertain to the legends in the section. These activities are followed by the actual legend, with review questions at the end.

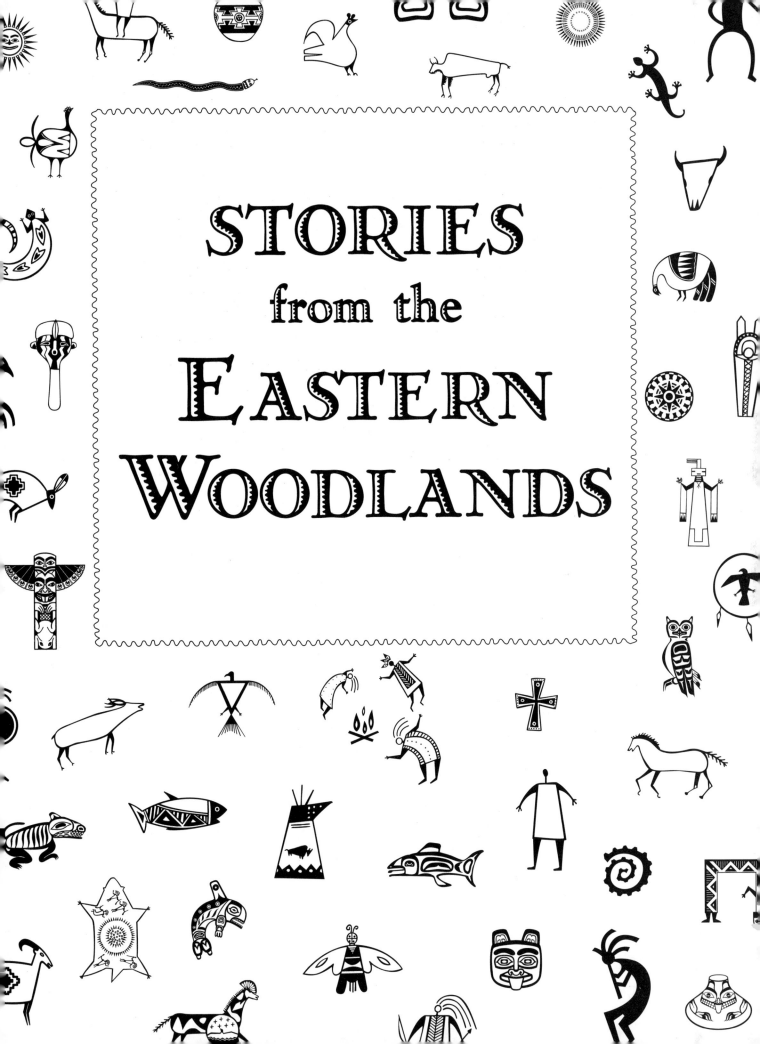

STORIES
from the
EASTERN
WOODLANDS

STORIES from the EASTERN WOODLANDS

Great Turtle Makes the World (Iroquois)

The Broken Wing (Chippewa)

Lone Bird, the Woman in the Moon (Chippewa)

Little People of the Micmac (Micmac)

The Origin of Corn (Abenaki)

Origin of the Pleiades (Cherokee)

How Deer Got His Horns (Cherokee)

When the early European settlers arrived in North America, they were met by Native Americans who lived along the heavily forested northeast coast. Today we often refer to these Native Americans as Woodland Indians. Though we consider the Woodland Indians as a group, it was actually made up of many individual groups. They included the Iroquois, Chippewa, Huron, Mohawk, Abenaki, Seneca, Micmac, Cherokee, Chickasaw, Creek, Seminole, and Natchez, to name just a few. They lived up and down the eastern coast of North America from just north of today's United States/Canadian border through Florida, and from the Atlantic coast to roughly just west of the Mississippi River.

The Woodland groups varied in many ways. While most lived in towns or villages, some lived in highly populated settings almost like cities. Their houses varied from wigwams in New England to the long houses of the

New York Iroquois. Most of these groups had some type of governing system. Some, such as the Iroquois were so highly organized, that our founding fathers borrowed some of their democratic ideas when forming the United States government.

When the first Europeans arrived in North America, most of the Woodland groups welcomed them. They even helped the new settlers through their early years in the new land. The Native Americans taught the settlers about the native foods and how to grow them, and how to hunt and fish. They shared many things with the new settlers— even their stories.

Many of their stories tell of the sacrifices that were made in the beginning so that our world could be, such as forming the earth in the Iroquois story "The Great Turtle Makes the World." Others tell of the lives lost to begin the heavenly bodies, as in the Chippewa story "Lone Bird, the Woman in the Moon," and the Abenaki story "Origin of the Pleiades." Many stories also focus on personal honor and duty as in the Chippewa story "The Broken Wing."

The stories told by these different groups are often similar. For example, the story of the origin of the earth told by the Iroquois, "Great Turtle Makes the World," is very similar to the story told by the Haida group; only the animals differ. Because of similarities it is hard to tell which group originated some stories. In some cases the story line is the same, but the characters are different, or the setting of the story differs.

The stories in this section include three creation, or origin, stories; an allegory in which a character stands for truth and loyalty; a story of magical Little People; a myth of how corn came to be; and a story of honesty versus deceit, or right being rewarded. The following is a brief synopsis of each of the legends in this section.

GREAT TURTLE MAKES THE WORLD

In this Iroquois legend, we learn how the Iroquois believe the earth, moon, and sun came to be. We hear of how many animals willingly offered their lives trying to provide a world for the First Woman. Then Little Turtle makes a perilous climb into the sky to collect lightning bolts and creates the sun and moon. This story was told in many different forms in various places in the eastern part of the United States and Canada. In some versions muskrat is the animal who finally succeeds in bringing up the dirt, and in others it is Grandmother Spider.

THE BROKEN WING

The Broken Wing is an allegory in which the main character, Grey Falcon, teaches about loyalty and responsibility. Grey Falcon, the elder brother, takes care of his baby siblings after their parents die. When Grey Falcon is hurt, his siblings do what is right and take care of him, just as he took care of them. Such stories usually made a point without lecturing, and would have been told with respect and gentleness as a guide to follow in life.

LONE BIRD, THE WOMAN IN THE MOON

Have you ever heard stories about the man in the moon? This Chippewa story is about a woman in the moon. The story was first recorded in 1848 by archaeologist Ephraim Squier, as it was told to him by George Copway, a chief of the Chippewa. The story explains how there came to be a "face" in the moon. A young girl named Lone Bird lives with her parents till they reach old age. Afraid of being alone when her parents die, Lone Bird wishes to be with the moon and gets her wish.

LITTLE PEOPLE OF THE MICMAC

Many stories of very small magical people having lived in North America are scattered throughout Native American literature. In this story a girl befriends a Little Person. The girl and her friends, after much prodding, agree to get into the Little People's canoes to go for a ride. As they step into the canoes, they shrink to the size of the Little People and travel across the river. Or, does the boat grow to fit them?

THE ORIGIN OF CORN

Today corn is one of the staple crops of the world. When Europeans first came to North America, corn had been grown and eaten here for at least 5,000 years. Because corn was so much a part of the lives of many Native Americans, they often told stories of how it was first obtained. This Abernaki corn story tells of a romance between a young girl and a lonely man and of his keeping a promise to her. The story explains how the silks growing out of the corn are believed to be strands from the young woman's hair.

ORIGIN OF THE PLEIADES

The Pleiades is a large cluster of stars in the constellation Taurus, six of which are visible to the naked eye. In this story, the Cherokee told how six boys became the heavenly bodies known as the Pleiades. They also explained the birth of the pine tree as coming from the earth where a boy fell and his mother cried.

HOW DEER GOT HIS HORNS

This Cherokee story shows that cheating gets you nowhere. In the story, Rabbit tries to trick the other animals by cheating in a race. When it is discovered that Rabbit was cheating, he is punished for what he has done. He must forfeit the race, and Deer wins the prize—a pair of horns that deer wear to this day.

CROSS-CURRICULAR ACTIVITIES

After students have read these legends, you may wish to have them do some of the following activities.

LANGUAGE ARTS/ART: Several of the legends in this section have to do with the origins of things such as the earth, the moon, the stars, and corn. Have students write their own legends about how one of these things (or something else) came to be. Have volunteers share their legends by reading them to the class. Students could also draw pictures to illustrate their legends.

LANGUAGE ARTS: Discuss the names of the characters in "Lone Bird, the Woman in the Moon." They are each named for some aspect of nature. Dawn of Day, the time when the sun rises in the east; She Eagle, the mother-nurturer; and Lone Bird, the cold and lonely young woman who wished to live out her life without the love of a man. Because the Native Americans were close to nature, the names they gave to themselves and their children were often related in some way to nature: an animal, bird, or manifestation of the elements. At other times, a person would be named after a personal characteristic or a deed that person had accomplished. Sometimes a name might be passed down from another family member or friend in the same way people do today. Have students think of new names for themselves based on something that is important to them, a characteristic of theirs, or based on nature. Discuss their choices. Have students explain how they picked their new name.

LANGUAGE ARTS: Just as the Micmac have legends about tiny people, other cultures also have similar kinds of legends. The Irish, for example, have stories about leprechauns. Other cultures have stories about trolls or elves. Have each student do research to find out about another legend about tiny people. Then have students share their legends with the class. Or, have students create their own stories about the escapades of tiny people who live in their backyard or in the school.

MATH: Corn is one of the many foods native to North America. Remnants of corn have been found in Indian ruins thousands of years old. Here is a simple corn muffin recipe for students to make after reading the legend "The Origin of Corn." Students can work in small groups or as a class with small groups doing different jobs. Be sure an adult puts the muffins into the oven and also takes them out.

INGREDIENTS:
    1 cup corn meal
    1 cup all-purpose flour
    1/4 cup sugar
    1 Tablespoon baking powder
    1 teaspoon salt
    1/3 cup vegetable oil
    1 whole egg or 2 egg whites
    1 cup milk

Have students measure and mix the dry ingredients in a bowl. Then have them combine the oil, egg, and milk together and stir the liquids into the dry ingredients. Pour the mixture into greased or sprayed muffin tins, filling each half way. Bake in hot oven 400°F. for 25 minutes or until done. Serve warm with butter and jam.

SCIENCE: There are many Native American stories about how certain groups of stars came to be. In "Origin of the Pleiades," students read about a specific constellation. A *constellation* is a group of stars the shape of which is said to resemble an animal or a mythological figure. For example, the constellation Orion, the Hunter in Greek mythology, is shaped like a bear. In an astronomy book or other reference book, have students find the Pleiades or another constellation. Then, using black construction paper and glitter or stick-on stars, have students create a copy of the constellation or make up one of their own. They can also find out something about the constellation and share it with the class.

Great Turtle Makes the World

Iroquois

Long ago before the world was as we know it now, the earth consisted of only water and darkness. The First People lived in the Sky World because there was no land on the earth. The chief of the Sky World, known as the Head Man, and his daughter lived in the Sky World. One day the Head Man's beloved daughter became ill. One after another, the best medicine people came to try to help her, but no one could cure her.

At last, the Head Man sought out an old wise man for help. The wise man told the Head Man to dig up a tree and place his daughter beside the hole. The people of the Sky World started digging up the tree when suddenly the tree fell right through the hole, taking the young woman with it. The Head Man had great power, but he did not have enough power to bring back his daughter.

Below the hole lay a vast expanse of water on which two swans floated in a dark sea world. Suddenly there was an enormous boom, which was the first thunder clap. When the swans looked up, they saw the sky opening and a tree falling down into the water. A woman fell into the water with the tree. The tree sank to the bottom of the water, but the swans swam over to the woman and held her up to keep her from sinking. She was so beautiful they did not want her to drown. The swans took the woman to the Great Turtle, who was the Head Animal. The Great Turtle called a council of all the animals.

When the animals arrived, the Great Turtle told them that the woman's coming indicated that good fortune was about to befall them. The tree had soil on its roots, and the Great Turtle told the animals to find where the tree had sunk and bring up some of the soil. With the soil he could make an island on his back for the woman, known as First Woman, to live upon.

The swans took all the animals to the place where the tree had fallen. Otter was the first to dive into the water to try to bring back some soil. Try as hard as he would, Otter could not reach the soil. Soon he floated to the top of the water, dead from exhaustion.

Muskrat was the next to try. He dove into the water and actually saw the tree, but it was so far away. By the time Muskrat got to the tree, he no longer had any strength, and he, too, died from exhaustion.

Next Beaver tried. He dove into the water, heading straight for the trunk of the tree. Gathering a small amount of soil in his paws, Beaver tried to rise to the surface of the water, but the soil melted away from his paws before he could get there. Beaver died just like the others.

After Beaver's body floated to the top of the water, the animals did not give up. Many of them dove deep into the water, but each one died from exhaustion. It seemed as though no one would be able to get the soil that First Woman needed. The animals almost gave up in despair.

Finally, Old Lady Toad, the meekest of all the animals, came to where the animals were diving.

"I would like to do my part," she said. "I cannot promise to get it, but please let me try."

"You are much too small," the others replied. "You'll never be able to stay down long enough to get the soil needed to build an earth."

"Nonetheless, I wish to do my small part," Old Lady Toad answered softly, and she dove into the water.

She stayed down so long the animals thought she, too, had failed just as they had feared she would. At last she surfaced, and just before she died she spat out a small mouthful of soil onto the back of the Great Turtle.

The soil she brought back had special powers, and it began to grow. It grew until it became a large island on the back of the Great Turtle. The animals gently placed the girl down upon the island. The two swans began to swim around the island until it grew into the earth as we now know it, and that is why we call our world Turtle Island.

Darkness still surrounded the earth, however, so the Great Turtle again called all the animals together in council. After discussing the problem of darkness for a long time, they decided to place a great light in the sky, but no one knew how to take the light up above the earth. Great Turtle called upon Little Turtle, who said she might be able to make the perilous climb into the sky, if each animal used his special power to help her.

The animals waited until a great dark cloud formed and began sending lightning out in every direction. Little Turtle climbed into the cloud and collected the lightning as she rode around the sky. Then she made a big ball of the lightning and threw it far up into the sky. Little Turtle liked the looks of the light but thought more was needed. So, Little Turtle gathered enough lightning to make another ball. The first ball, which was larger, she called Sun, and the second ball she called Moon.

Then Great Turtle told the animals to make holes in the sky. Now the sun and moon could each go down through one hole and come up again through the other hole as they went around the earth, giving us day and night. ▫

Questions to Think About

1. *The animals did not think Old Lady Toad could get the soil because she was small. Why did the animals think her size would have kept her from doing the job?*

2. *After seeing several animals die, why do you think others continued to dive for the soil?*

3. *Why do you think Little Turtle obeyed Great Turtle?*

From Burland, Cottie. *North American Indian Mythology.* The Hamlyn Publishing Group LTD, Middlesex, England, 1965, and various other sources.

The Broken Wing

Chippewa

A hunter shot two falcons, leaving six young falcons alone in a nest. Since only one of the young birds was able to fly, the little falcons depended on their parents for food. Now they waited in vain for their parents to return with their food.

Grey Falcon, the oldest of the brood, and the only one with feathers strong enough to carry him through the air, took over the care of his younger siblings. All summer long he found and caught food for the young falcons. When the leaves of autumn began to turn to gold and red, the young falcons talked of leaving for a warmer climate in the south. By now, even the youngest ones had learned to fly.

But one day a tragedy befell Grey Falcon. Just when he was pouncing on a swan, which would have given them all delicious food, he broke his wing and could not return to the nest. After waiting some time for his return, the younger falcons went in search of Grey Falcon. They found him lying helpless beside the lake.

"I cannot fly," he said. "You must go on ahead to the south. It is better that I, alone, should die, than that the rest of you should also be threatened."

"No!" the young ones cried in unison. "We will not desert you. You took care of us when our parents died, and now we shall take care of you!"

The young falcons found a hollow tree to which they gently carried their older brother. They stored up enough food to last through the winter. To help the food last longer, two of the young birds flew south leaving Grey Falcon in the care of the other three.

Grey Falcon gradually recovered from his wound. In the lengthening days of advancing spring, he began to teach the young ones to hunt. They were all successful in their search for fresh food, except Pigeon Hawk. He was the youngest and very foolish. Pigeon Hawk spent his days flying around from place to place, always returning without a morsel of food for himself or the others. He depended on the others to support him.

Grey Falcon had great patience, but finally he called Pigeon Hawk to his side and said, "Why are you having such poor luck in your hunting, younger brother?"

"I am small and weak," the younger one replied. "I kill ducks and birds each time I hunt, but just as I get near home, Owl comes up behind me and snatches away what I have caught."

"I see," Grey Falcon said. "Tomorrow I shall go with you."

The following day Grey Falcon accompanied his younger brother as far as the lake. Then he landed on the shore and waited for Pigeon Hawk to return from his hunt. He saw Pigeon Hawk seize a duck, and just as he was approaching the shore with his prey, Owl darted out from the shadows of the trees and took the duck from Pigeon Hawk's claws. Grey Falcon sprang up and grabbed hold of Owl forcefully and started toward home with him.

Pigeon Hawk followed the older hawk home, full of anger at what Owl had been doing to him. He flew into Owl's face, ready to tear out his eyes, but Grey Falcon placed his own wing protectively in front of Owl to ward off the blows.

"No, my younger brother," he said. "Do not look for revenge. This will serve as a lesson to Owl to not pick on someone smaller than he is."

Grey Falcon proceeded to give Owl some good advice, including which herbs to use to cure his wounds. Then Grey Falcon set Owl free.

The two young hawks who had gone south for the winter arrived just then, and all the young birds chose mates and flew into the woods to make their own homes. Spring had arrived. The streams bubbled joyfully down the hills, and young green leaves began to sprout from the trees. The Good Spirit had shown kindness and preserved the young falcons through the cold of winter, just as Grey Falcon had shown kindness by not killing his enemy the Owl. ⊡

Questions to Think About

1. Why do you think Grey Falcon and his siblings were willing to help and look out for each other?

2. How do people in families look out for and help each other?

From Clark, Ella Elizabeth. *Indian Legends of Canada*. McClelland and Stewart Ltd., 1960.

Lone Bird, the Woman in the Moon

Chippewa

Many snows before Europeans came to change the land, the Chippewa were a proud and prosperous people. Hunters of the buffalo on the plains, trappers of the beavers in the lakes, and hunters of the deer in forests of the Great Lakes, they were feared, loved, and respected by all other peoples.

At that time, a girl named Lone Bird lived along the shores of Lake Superior. She lived with her father, Dawn of Day, and her mother, She Eagle. Lone Bird was an only child and the most beautiful and graceful of all the young women in her village. Young men came from far and wide trying to gain her consent to marriage. But Lone Bird was content living with her parents and looked down with scorn upon the young men's requests.

The young men told Lone Bird stories of their success as hunters and their acts of bravery, but to no avail. Lone Bird's heart remained cold to their pleas. The disappointed young men always returned to their homes saddened and alone.

Her Father, Dawn of Day, praised the skill of the young men who wanted to marry Lone Bird. He told her how fortunate she was to have young men with such excellent reputations seeking her heart. Lone Bird merely laughed and said, "I have my mother to love me and my father to protect me. Why should I give that up to take care of a man?"

Dawn of Day listened sadly, for he worried about his beautiful daughter. After giving it much thought, he devised a plan. Dawn of Day called all the young men of the village together and told them, "I wish to plan a race on the shores of the great lake called Lake Superior. The winner of this race, the one who proves to be the swiftest of foot, shall have my daughter's hand in marriage."

The young men were overjoyed, for each of them wanted to marry Lone Bird, and they began training for the race. News of the contest spread far and wide through all the villages of the Chippewa. On the morning of the race, a huge crowd gathered to watch to see who would win.

The old men of the village were chosen to judge the winner and award the prize. The contestants came in droves, painted and dressed in their best clothes. The other young women of the Chippewa Nation came to catch the attention of the young men who lost the race. Lone Bird was the only one who did not go to see the race. She remained weeping in her parents' home.

The race began. The young men lined up at the appointed place. At the sound of the starting signal, they dashed ahead. Two runners quickly ran to the head of the group. Bending Bow and Who-strikes-the-game had each loved Lone Bird since childhood. They were sleek as the deer and swift as the wind. When they reached the finish line, the judges could not tell which one had come in first. So the two ran again, and yet a third time. Each time it was a tie.

Someone suggested that they have a jumping contest, but when this was tried, they again finished as equals.

"Let them have a contest of hunting skill," another villager offered. So the two went off to different parts of the forest. At the end of the day, Bending Bow and Who-strikes-the-game each returned with the skins of twenty bears, which they placed at the feet of the judges.

Now Dawn of Day was very troubled. He knew the Great Spirit surely had his hand in the results of the contests, and the saddened father returned home questioning what he should do. Lone Bird still sat in her place in the lodge. Her eyes were red and swollen from weeping, and her head was downcast. Dawn of Day was unhappy, because he truly adored his lovely daughter, but he did not know what to do.

"Daughter, you weep," he said as he took her face in his hands.

"Why do you wish to send me away?" she replied. "Is your home too small for me to remain? I do not wish to leave you."

"You never shall," he promised, for he could refuse Lone Bird nothing.

He went out to the people who had gathered outside his home and told them, "The contest is over. Bending Bow and Who-strikes-the-game have competed fairly and well, but the Great Spirit has decided that Lone Bird shall remain in the home of her parents."

All the villagers returned to their homes, and the sad young men turned slowly away.

Summer and autumn came and went and winter returned to the land. When the snows at last melted, and the spring flowers began to bloom, Lone Bird went with Dawn of Day to tap the juice of the maple trees. Later, as the smoke curled up from the fire, the young woman sat on a rock and looked around at the signs of spring. The sun shined down kindly upon her, but her heart was very heavy. She could see that the hair of her parents was turning grey. She knew that soon they would feel the aches and pains of old age and that she would one day be left alone.

"What will I do when they are gone?" she thought. "I have no brothers, no sisters, no one to stay by me as I, too, grow older."

Suddenly, for the first time in her life, she felt fear and loneliness. Lone Bird looked at the spring flowers, always in pairs, each flower adding its beauty to that of the other. Birds were building their nests, again in pairs. The creatures of earth all seemed to be in pairs.

"Only I will be living alone," thought Lone Bird, and she felt more alone than ever. She sadly recalled how she turned away the young men who had wanted to marry her. Still, she did not wish to join her life with that of another. "Why did the Good Spirit not give me a heart like those of others? Why am I doomed to live alone?" she asked herself.

For many hours Lone Bird sat on a rock until the sun's rays fell behind the trees. The moon's silvery path was shining across the surface of the lake when she finally stood and looked longingly at the moon in its far place in the sky. "How I would like to be with you," she thought. "If I had your love, I would no longer be lonely."

The Good Spirit heard her desire, and in an instant she was carried up to the moon.

Meanwhile, Dawn of Day had finished his work, and seeing that Lone Bird was no longer seated on the rock, he assumed she had returned to the village. Not finding her at home, Dawn of Day went back to where he had last seen Lone Bird. He called her name, but no one answered.

Sadly, and with much fear, his eyes were drawn to the moon, and there he saw her. He mourned no more, for he knew she would always be cared for lovingly.

Many moons and many snows have passed since Dawn of Day saw his daughter in the arms of the moon. The Chippewa are no longer numerous, and others now live on the land which once was theirs. But when spring returns to the Great Lakes each year, the same flowers bloom, and Lone Bird smiles down upon the people as they tell her story by the fires. ▢

Questions to Think About

1. Why did Lone Bird not want to get married?

2. What was Lone Bird afraid of near the end of the story?

3. Do you think Lone Bird did the right thing by going up to the moon? What else could she have done to escape her loneliness?

4. Why did Lone Bird's father accept her leaving so easily?

5. Do you think Lone Bird was happy with the moon? Why?

From Clark, Ella Elizabeth. *Indian Legends of Canada.* Copyright Canada, by McClelland and Stewart Ltd., 1960.

Little People of the Micmac

Micmac

The Little People look like tiny human beings. Most of them live in small caves or in burrows in the ground. Sometimes, if it is very quiet and you listen closely, you can hear them walking in the forest. Usually the Little People stay indoors during the day and only come out at night. When they do come out, they love to dance and have parties. They sing and play the drums and have a jolly good time. At times the Little People do good things to help people, but sometimes they are full of mischief. The Little People are said to have the power to shrink you down to their size. When you leave them, however, you will go back to your normal size.

The mischievous Little People love to play jokes on people. When you are very busy, one of them might sneak in and take something you need. Then they hide behind something and giggle as you look all over for the item. Later, they slip the item back to where it had been before you started looking for it.

Once, a long time ago, a girl was playing and swimming at the edge of the river when she noticed a tiny canoe floating down the river. It was being paddled by a tiny little man. She was curious and wanted to play with him, so she picked him up and took him home.

When her parents saw what she had in her hands, they became very frightened and said, "Take him back where you found him right now! Let him go!"

The girl was very disappointed, for he was like a little live doll. She did as her parents told her, but only after playing with him for awhile. Finally, she set the little man and his canoe back into the river where she had found them. She watched as he floated down the river. The girl and the little man waved to each other, and before passing out of sight, he told her he would come back sometime.

Every day the girl would watch for the little man to reappear. One day, as she was picking berries with some other girls by the river, she saw a dozen little canoes coming down the river. The little man she had played with was a chief, and he had brought some of his people back with him. They pulled up their canoes to the side of the river and began to cook a meal. When they finished eating, they told the girls, "If you want to go to the other side of the river, we will take you there in our canoes."

The girls thought that was funny and said, "We cannot ride in your canoes! They are too small!"

The Little People tried to get the girls to get into the canoes, but the girls just laughed at them. Finally the little chief asked the girl who had first found him to get into the canoe. To humor him the little girl agreed. Lo and behold, as soon as she put her foot into the canoe, the little boat appeared to grow to be the size people like her would use. Her friends on shore were amazed, for now she and the canoe both looked tiny.

The girl tried to persuade her friends to climb into the canoes, too. Seeing that the girl arrived safely on the other side of the river, the other girls did as she asked. The Little People took them all across the river, and as soon as they stepped ashore, the little boats sailed on down the river, never to be seen again. No one knows how the girls got back to their side of the river. ▫

From Clark, Ella Elizabeth. *Indian Legends of Canada.* McCelland and Stewart Ltd., 1960.

Questions to Think About

1. *Why did the girl return the tiny man to the river?*

2. *If you were one of the girls in the story, would you have gotten into the canoe? Why?*

3. *How do you think you would have viewed these events—would the girl have shrunk or would the canoe have grown?*

The Origin of Corn

Abenaki

Long ago, a man lived far away from other people. He did not know about fire, so he ate only roots, barks, and nuts. Being alone all the time, he became quite lonely. "If only I had someone to share my life," he sometimes thought to himself.

After some time he grew tired of looking around for food in the woods and stopped eating. He lay under the sun dreaming. One day when he awoke, he saw a young woman standing nearby. Her hair was golden and unlike any hair he had ever seen. When she spoke, her voice sounded like singing.

He immediately fell in love with her, and he asked her to come to him. She would not do this, however, and when he tried to go near her, she backed away. This only made him want her more, and he began to sing a song of loneliness to her.

"Please do not leave me!" he begged. "If you will only stay, I will do anything you ask me to do."

At first she said nothing. Then she took pity on the unhappy man and said to him, "Will you promise to do anything I ask of you?"

"Oh, yes!" he replied eagerly. "Just say what it is you want me to do, and I promise to move the earth if I have to just to please you."

She led him to a place where there was much dry grass. "Please get me two very dry sticks," she told him, and he did it right away.

The woman rubbed the sticks

29

together very quickly in the grass. Before the man could blink his eyes, a spark flew out and the grass caught fire. The fire burned all the grass until only a black patch lay where the grass had been.

"When the sun sets," the young woman said, "Take me by the hair and drag me over this burned ground."

The man was aghast, as you can imagine. "I could not do anything like that," he said.

"You promised you would do anything I ask," the young woman reminded him.

He did not want to do it, but he finally agreed to do as she asked.

She told him, "After you have dragged me over this ground, you will see a plant which looks something like grass. When you see my hair coming from behind the leaves you will know that the seeds in the plant can be used for food."

With a heavy heart he did as she told him. To this day, when Native Americans see the silks on the corn, they know that these are from the hair of the young woman and that she has not forgotten them. □

Questions to Think About

1. *Why did the man promise the young woman he would do anything she asked?*

2. *Why do you think the young woman gave him the gift of corn?*

3. *The young woman in the story made the man drag her across the ground instead of just giving him the corn. Why do you think she did that?*

4. *Why do you think the Abenaki developed a legend about the origin of corn?*

From Thompson, Stith. *Tales of the North American Indians.* Indiana University Press, 1929. Originally from Brown, *Journal of American Folk-lore*, 214.

Origin of the Pleiades

Cherokee

A very long time ago there lived seven young boys. These boys liked to play a game in which they used a curved stick to roll a stone hoop along the ground. These boys wanted to do nothing else but play this game. Day after day their mothers scolded them, telling them their help was needed in the cornfields. But the boys continued to play.

One evening, while cooking corn for dinner, the mothers put some of the game hoops into the cooking pots and boiled them along with the corn. They then served the stone hoops and corn to the boys and told them, "Since you like these stone hoops so much, you can have them for dinner."

The boys were very angry with their mothers for what they had done. They complained to each other, saying, "Since our mothers treat us so badly, let us go to a place where we will not bother them any longer."

The boys went down to the village meeting house and began to dance around it. Around and around the building they danced, crying out for the spirits to help them.

Worried about where the boys were and what they were doing, their mothers went to look for them. There at the village meeting house, they found the boys dancing around the building. The mothers watched the boys dance faster and faster, and soon the feet of the boys were leaving the ground. The boys were rising higher and higher into the air each time they circled the building.

Horrified, the mothers ran to get their sons, but the boys had already gone so high as to be over the roof of the meeting house. One boy's mother, however, was able to grab her son's feet and pull him down. The boy fell so hard that he sank into the ground, and the Earth covered him up.

The other six boys continued to rise farther and farther into the sky, until they could only be seen as stars. Today these stars are called the Pleiades, but the Cherokee know them as *Anit'sutsa,* the Boys.

The mothers mourned the loss of their sons. The mother of the boy who sank into the Earth came twice a day to cry over the spot where he had fallen. The Earth remained damp from her tears, and one day a little green shoot grew up out of the Earth. This shoot grew and grew until it became the tree we call the pine. Today the Cherokee believe the pine holds within itself the nature of the stars and the same bright light which we see when we light a fire. ▫

Questions to Think About

1. *Why did the boys leave their mothers?*

2. *Do the boys in the story behave like children today? How?*

3. *What natural features does this story explain?*

4. *Who do you think suffered more, the boys or their mothers? Why?*

5. *Do you think the boys were happier as stars than as boys? Write a letter from a star boy to his mother, telling what his life is like and how he feels as a star.*

From Mooney, James. *Myths of the Cherokee*. Charles and Randy Elder-Booksellers Publishers, Nashville, Tennessee, 1982. Stories originally collected by Mooney during the 1880's and published about 1890.

How Deer Got His Horns

Cherokee

Long ago Deer did not have horns. His head was smooth and soft, just like the doe's head. Deer was as quick on his feet as Rabbit was a good jumper. The animals often wondered who would win if Deer and Rabbit should have a race.

One day the animals arranged a race between Deer and Rabbit. The object of the contest was to begin at one side of a thick tangle of brush, go through it, and then come back. The prize for winning was to be a beautiful pair of antlers.

The antlers were very soft and velvety, and both Deer and Rabbit wanted them. On the day of the race all the animals came. The antlers were displayed on the ground at the edge of the brush, as they were to provide the starting point. Noticing how the other animals admired the antlers made Rabbit want them all the more.

"If I had those antlers, I would be even better looking than I am now," Rabbit thought to himself. He was now determined to win the antlers.

Then Rabbit said aloud, "I am a stranger in these parts. I need to look around through the brush to get the lay of the land before the race."

"Go right ahead," everyone said, for they wanted to be fair. They did not know that Rabbit was a trickster.

Rabbit went into the brush. After he was gone for a long time, the animals realized that he must be up to something.

"We'd better send someone to look for Rabbit," someone said. "He may be up to some mischief."

So the animals sent someone to look for him. Way down in the brush they found Rabbit. He was gnawing down the overgrowth and clearing a path at just his height to make it easier for him to run fast. When the others heard what Rabbit had been doing, they said to him, "Friend Rabbit, it seems that you have been cheating."

Rabbit denied this, but when the road was inspected, his work was exposed for all to see.

"Friend Rabbit," they said to him, "you were trying to cheat. You must forfeit the race. Deer wins the antlers!" The animals gave the beautiful antlers to Deer, who has worn them at certain times of the year ever since.

As for Rabbit, he was told that from that time on he would have to cut down brush for a living, which he still does. ▫

Questions to Think About

1. Why was a race being held between Rabbit and Deer?

2. Do you think it was fair to Deer to let Rabbit look over the race course? Why?

3. In your opinion, what is the lesson of this legend?

4. From what happened in the story, do you think the Cherokee thought cheating was acceptable?

5. Do you think Rabbit learned his lesson?

From Mooney, James. *Myths of the Cherokee.* Charles and Randy Elder-Booksellers Publishers, Nashville, Tennessee, 1982. Mooney originally collected these stories during the 1880's from elderly Cherokee, and they were first published around 1890.

STORIES
from the
GREAT
PLAINS

STORIES from the GREAT PLAINS

Old Man Teaches the People (Blackfoot)

White Buffalo Woman (Sioux)

The Boy and the Turtles (Sioux)

The area known as the Great Plains stretches from central Canada in the North to Mexico in the South, and from the Rocky Mountains in the West to the Mississippi in the East. Many different groups lived in this area, including the Arapaho, Arikara, Blackfeet, Cheyenne, Comanche, Crow, Kiowa, Omaha, Pawnee, Sioux, and Wichita to name a few. There were many different lifestyles among these groups. Some were wanderers who followed the buffalo all year. Others lived in permanent villages, going out on short hunts and returning to the village. But the horse and buffalo were very important to all of these groups.

The peoples who inhabited the Great Plains are the ones many people visualize when they think of Native Americans. They picture tall, straight-backed chiefs wearing trailing feathered headdresses, riding on painted ponies, smoking ceremonial pipes, living in tipis, and going on the warpath. Like many other ideas about the first peoples of North America, this picture is a stereotype.

It is true that there were Indian chiefs who occasionally wore headdresses and went to war, but that was only one part of what the Indians of the Great Plains were. Like other people, the people of the Plains fell in love, married, raised families whom they loved, and mourned their dead. Many of their stories are about these everyday occurrences.

The stories told by the people of the Great Plains were very imaginative. Some stories taught lessons while others were simply for entertainment. Like other groups, they told stories of how the earth was made, and of the sun, moon, and stars. But they also told tales of mystery and romance and tales intended to teach children the correct ways to behave. They told stories of the Little People and the supernatural. They also told stories about tricksters, heroes, horses, and customs.

The stories taught the values the people believed were important for the children to learn. Many of their stories involve buffalo which were very important to their survival. The first story in this section tells how the world, including the buffalo, came to be; the last story tells how the buffalo disappeared. The second story focuses on the sacred peace pipe and the path on which it leads you to goodness. The third story is about Little People. Just as the Woodlands told stories about the Little People, so did the people of the Plains.

The following is a brief synopsis of each of the legends in this section.

OLD MAN TEACHES THE PEOPLE

There are many stories about Old Man, whom some Native Americans call Old-man-coyote. Some stories are about how Old Man created the world, and others show him as a trickster. In this Blackfoot story, Old Man creates the world and people. Then he teaches the people how to make weapons and hunt buffalo. He also teaches them how to make clothing from buffalo skins and how to make fire. Old Man tells the people that through their dreams they can find the power to control their lives.

WHITE BUFFALO WOMAN

To the Native Americans the smoking of the ceremonial pipe was a sacred ritual. In this Sioux story, we learn how they first obtained the pipe, sometimes referred to as the "peace pipe," and why it is smoked. The people are also shown how to honor the sky, earth, and the four directions by offering the pipe to these places. The story also shows how bad things will happen to you if you think bad thoughts about people. The destruction of the man with the bad thoughts symbolizes that no good comes from thinking badly about someone.

THE BOY AND THE TURTLES

Like the Micmac story, this Sioux story is about the Little People. In this story a young boy sees a group of turtles enter a lake and come out as little men. After reporting this sighting to his elders, the boy is looked upon as being very special and spiritual. He is now treated with reverence and given a new name to symbolize his new status.

CROSS-CURRICULAR ACTIVITIES

After students have read these legends, you may wish to have them do some of the following activities.

ART: In *Old Man Teaches the People,* students learned how the bow and arrow came to be. Later on people also learned to use shields to protect themselves. Made of rawhide that had been toughened until it was very hard, the shield was usually about 15 to 18 inches in diameter. It was decorated with drawings and/or symbols of what the warrior believed to be his own special powers. It might have feathers, paintings of great deeds, or animals, or other things. Have students design a shield they would use if they lived during this time. Have them use symbols that stand for themselves. Then on construction paper or oak tag, have students transfer the design and decorate the shield using paint, markers, glitter, or other available materials. Display the finished shields as students give brief explanations of what the symbols represent.

MUSIC: In *White Buffalo Woman,* the woman sings a song about walking before she changes into a buffalo. Have students make up a song about buffalo that communicates the great reverence the people had for this animal. Have volunteers share their songs with the class.

LANGUAGE ARTS: In *The Boy and the Turtles,* students heard about a boy who was given honors because he had seen the Little People. Have students imagine that they are the boy in this story, and have them rewrite the story from the point at which the Little People come out of the water. Rather than the boy's running away have them, take the boy on a further adventure. Give them suggestions on where to go with the story by asking questions such as: What happens next? Do they communicate? Does he follow the people? Does he learn a great secret about the world? and so on.

Old Man Teaches the People

Blackfoot

First, Old Man made the world and the people. He covered the plains with grass for the animals to eat. He made all kinds of roots and berries and trees. Then he thought he would make human beings. He made them out of clay.

Old Man showed the people how to eat berries and roots. He told them that animals and birds were good to eat. He told them they could eat the bark of certain trees, too. He thought that he had told them everything they needed to know to live, and so he went away for awhile.

When he came back, Old Man looked at the people he had made, and things were not as they should be. Big brown animals with beards and horns (buffalo) were chasing the people. Sometimes the animals caught and ate the people.

Old Man said to himself, "This is not right! I have to change this. These people do not know how to live. They let the buffalo eat them, instead of the other way around. I must show them that they should be eating the buffalo!"

He had a big job to do. Old Man began by again showing the people which roots, berries, barks, and other plant foods were good to eat. He also told them that they should be eating the buffalo, not letting the buffalo eat them.

But the people cried out, "How could we do this? We have no weapons. These animals are bigger than we are and they have sharp horns."

So Old Man said, "All right. I will make you weapons with which to kill these animals."

Old Man went out and cut some sarvis berry shoots. First he stripped off the bark of the shoots. Then he flattened a long piece of wood and made a bow by tying a thin stringlike material to it. He put four bird feathers on the end of the weapon, which he called an arrow, but it would not fly. He took the feathers off the arrow and tried using three feathers instead. This time it flew. Old Man found some small pieces of black stone and broke sharp pieces off. He chipped away at the pieces making points. Then he put the points on the arrow on the opposite end from the feathers.

Then he said, " From now on do not run away from the animals and do not let them eat you. Take these arrows with you, and when the animals get close to you, shoot these arrows at the animals."

The people did what Old Man told them to do. At first, when the animals ran toward them, they were not fast enough, and some people died. The people practiced and practiced, and pretty soon they were able to shoot the buffalo. Once the buffalo had been killed, the people did not know what to do with them. Old Man then showed the people how to make stone knives to cut up the buffalo meat. He also showed them how to make tools for scraping and cleaning the skins. Then he showed the people how to use the skins of the buffalo to make clothing so they would not be so cold in winter.

Next Old Man showed the people how to make fire so they could cook the buffalo meat. He gathered soft dry wood and mashed it up. Then he took a piece of hard wood and drilled a hole in it to make fire sticks. He showed the people how to rub the wood together until sparks shot out onto the soft dry wood starting a fire. Now the people could cook the animals and eat them.

Old Man also told the people how they could gain power through the animals in their dreams. He said, "When an animal appears to you in a dream, you must do what he tells you. If you need help and cry out loud for help, the animal will help you, and you must listen to him. This way, you will get his power, for every animal has power."

Old Man also taught the people how to set up poles and make tipis with the buffalo skins. And then he went around the country making more people and showing them how to live, too. And it was good.

Later on, Old Man marked off some lines and said, "This is your land I have made for you. Do not let other people come into it, because it is just for you. This land is for the five tribes [Blackfeet, Bloods, Piegans, Gros Ventres, and Sarcees], and you will need to fight anyone who tries to take it from you."

Our forefathers fought anyone who tried to get into our land and kept them out. Later, however, we let the new settlers come here. In this we disobeyed Old Man's laws, and we have been punished for it.

When Old Man was through making the world and making people and teaching them how to live, he lay down on a hill near Red Deer's River and rested. You can still see him resting there. ▫

Questions to Think About

1. What did Old Man create?

2. Why did Old Man teach the people to make arrows?

3. Why do you think Old Man told the people not to let others on their land?

4. Do you think Old Man would be disappointed in the way his people took care of their land? Why?

5. How does this legend of how the world came to be differ from the Woodland version told in Great Turtle Makes the World? Which legend seems more realistic? Why?

From Grinnell, George Bird. *Blackfoot Lodge Tales.* University of Nebraska Press, Lincoln and London, 1962. Originally published by Charles Scribner's Sons, 1892.

White Buffalo Woman

Lakota Sioux

In the very early days of the people, two scouts left camp to look for buffalo. There had been little food for the people. They traveled until they came to a high hill. Looking to the north, the scouts saw a woman approaching in the distance.

"It is a woman!" the first one said. Immediately, this man began to have bad thoughts about the woman.

"Do not think bad thoughts about this woman," the second scout cautioned, as though reading the mind of the other. "This woman is sacred. Throw your bad thoughts away."

As the woman came nearer, the men could see that she wore the finest white buckskin clothing. Her hair was very long and shining black, and she was beautiful. This woman was able to see into the minds of the men. When she spoke, the woman's voice sounded like singing.

She saw the bad thoughts that the first man was thinking. As the first man came near her, a white cloud came down from the sky and covered them both. The beautiful woman walked out of the cloud. When the cloud blew away, only a skeleton remained where the man had been.

The woman next spoke to the second man, telling him, "Go home and tell your people I am coming. Have them build for me a big tipi in the center of the nation."

The man was afraid, so he left quickly. When he told the people about the woman, they immediately followed the woman's instructions. Before long the woman came, and the people were in awe of her, for she was very lovely. She sang a song as she went into the tipi.

As she sang, she breathed a white cloud with a wonderful smell. She gave the chief a sacred pipe. On one side of the pipe, a buffalo calf was carved. This symbolized the earth that bears and sustains us. Twelve eagle feathers hung from the stem to represent the sky and the twelve moons. These feathers were tied with unbreakable ties of grass.

"Behold," the woman said. "With this pipe you will multiply and become a great nation. Only good will come from the pipe if you follow the path it shows you. Only good hands shall care for it, and bad eyes shall not see it."

The woman sang her song again. Then as the people watched, she quickly walked from the tipi. Suddenly, before the eyes of the people, the woman changed into a white buffalo that galloped away, never to be seen again. But the lands around the Sioux were now full of buffalo.

Now when Indians light the pipe, they offer it up to honor the powers that rule the world. First, to the One Above, the Great Spirit. Next, they offer the pipe to the four directions, and finally, to the Earth.

And when they smoke the pipe, they believe there can be only good between them. No lies and no bad thoughts. ▫

From Neihardt, John G. *Black Elk Speaks*. University of Nebraska Press, 1961. Originally published by William Morrow & Company, 1932. This story was told to the author by Black Elk, an old Oglala holy man. There are various other versions in other sources, but all are substantially the same.

Questions to Think About

1. Why do you think the man with the bad thoughts was destroyed?

2. Why do you think the symbols on the pipe were of the earth and sky?

3. Why do the Native Americans think that those who share the pipe shall have no bad thoughts?

4. Who do you think the woman in this story was? Why?

The Boy and the Turtles

Sioux

A young boy went on a turtle hunt. At first he hoped to find some turtles in a creek. He followed along several different streams without any luck. At last he decided that he would only be able to find them in the lake.

When he arrived at the lake, the boy got down on his hands and knees. You see, the turtles were wary of strangers, and the boy did not want to alarm the turtles. He peeped over a rock and saw a large number of turtles sunning themselves. He very quietly took off his clothes so he could dive quickly into the water. While removing his shirt, one of his hands went up too high, and the turtles saw him and jumped into the lake.

The boy ran to the water, but only bubbles came up from the bottom of the lake. Then suddenly the boy saw a Little Man climbing up out of the water. The first Little Man was soon followed by many others. It seemed as though there were hundreds of them splashing and playing in the water. Afraid, the boy ran for home, leaving his clothing by the lake.

The boy fell into the door of his grandmother's lodge. "What is wrong, child?" the woman said. The boy was still so frightened he could not speak.

"What did you see that scared you so much?" she asked again. The boy's fright had closed his throat so that he still could not tell her what was wrong. He began beating his sides with his fists. The grandmother got out her medicine bundle. She tended to the boy with her medicine and then prayed to Wakan Tanka to drive out the evil spirit that she thought had entered her grandson's body. The woman's medicine and prayer worked, and soon the boy was able to tell her what he had seen.

The grandmother went to the lodge of the chief and told him what her grandson had said. The chief sent two of his bravest warriors to the lake to see whether the boy's story was true. The braves walked very quietly to the lake. At the lake they saw Little Men swimming and splashing just as the boy had said. The warriors were frightened, and they hurried home to tell the chief and the council what they had seen.

The chief asked for the boy to be brought to the council. The boy, now looked upon as being spiritual, was given the seat of honor opposite the door. He was given a new name, Wankan Wanyanka, which means "sees holy," and the lake was renamed Man Lake. ▫

From McLaughlin, Marie. *Myths and Legends of the Sioux*. University of Nebraska Press, 1990. Originally published Bismark, ND, 1916. McLaughlin was the part Sioux wife of Indian agent James McLaughlin.

Questions to Think About

1. What was the boy hunting for?

2. What is the relationship between the turtles and the Little Men?

3. Why did the grandmother think the boy had an evil spirit in him?

4. Why did the council treat the boy with honor after he ran away scared?

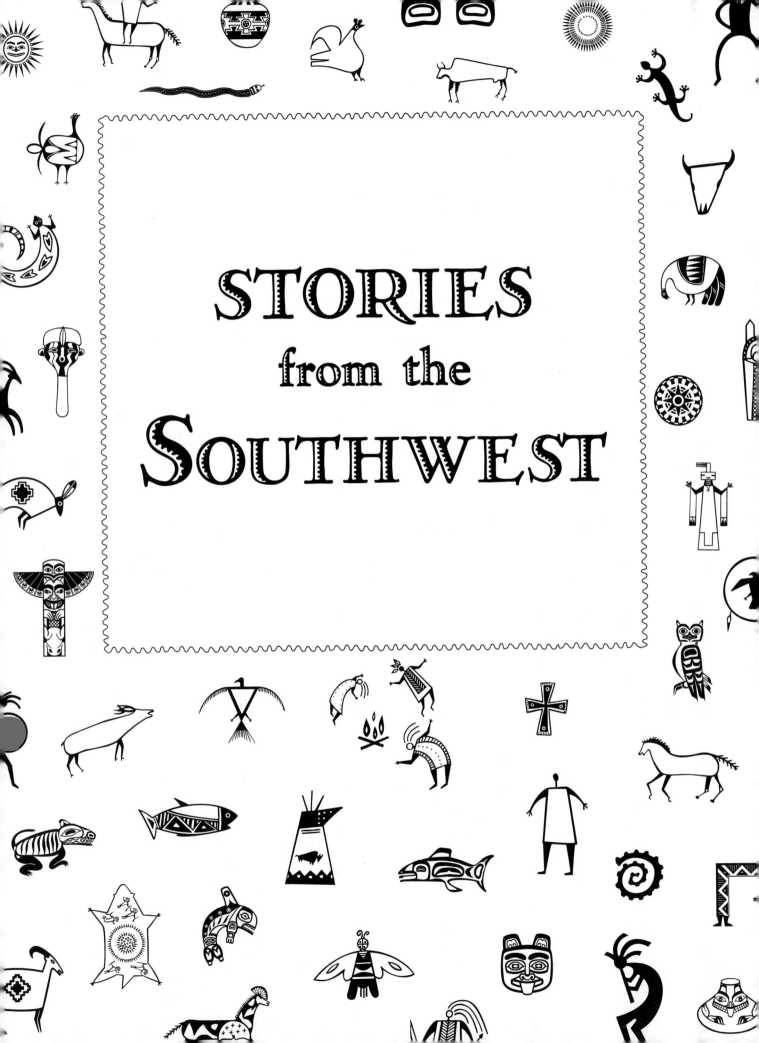

STORIES
from the
SOUTHWEST

STORIES from the SOUTHWEST

Coyote and the Woodpeckers (Pueblo)

The Mother Moon (Pueblo)

Turkey Makes Corn and Coyote Plants It (Apache)

The Coyote and the Bear (Pueblo)

The Native Americans of the Southwest lived in what are now the states of Arizona, New Mexico, and southern Utah, as well as northern Mexico. They include the Apache, Cochimi, Navajo, Pueblo, Quechan, and Yaqui, to name a few. For the most part, this region is very dry and rain is very important to the people.

The Native American groups read about so far tended to have many similarities among the groups in their region; this is not true in the Southwest. The Native Americans in this region were very different from each other.

Some, like the Apaches and Comanches who roamed about hunting buffalo and riding horses, were in many ways like the people of the Plains. Others, like the Pueblo, were farmers. Even the housing in the Southwest varied. The Pueblo peoples built houses from mud bricks, the Navajos lived in round houses called hogans, while the Apache lived in tipis or brush huts. Their stories were as varied as the construction of their houses.

Three of the four stories in this section are legends from the Pueblo people. The Pueblo people lived in villages and had a highly developed civilization. They were peaceful people who fought only when attacked and had many religious ceremonies. To the Pueblo, the sun and moon gods ranked above all others and appeared in many legends as in *The Mother Moon*. Other legends taught that certain ways were not good, as in *The Coyote and the Woodpeckers* and *The Coyote and the Bear*. The coyote was a popular character found in many Native American legends, and he was generally looked upon as being sneaky and untrustworthy.

Unlike the Pueblo, the Apache were aggressive, generally raiding other groups for food. They did not have permanent homes, choosing to live in tipis and brush huts. The other story in this section is an Apache legend, *Turkey Makes Corn and Coyote Plants It*. This story shows the importance of providing for oneself and being self-dependent.

All of the stories in this section teach a lesson in life, such as putting loved ones first, being yourself rather than putting on false airs, thinking things through before taking action, and learning how to take care of yourself. These are all lessons that can be found in the legends of many other Native American groups.

The following is a brief synopsis of each of the legends in this section.

COYOTE AND THE WOODPECKERS

Snobbery and jealousy are the focus of this Pueblo story. In nature a coyote is rather sneaky, and many find him unattractive. The woodpecker, on the other hand, is neat and pretty. In this story Father Coyote misinterprets the Woodpeckers' actions and sees them as putting on airs because they are prettier than he. Upset and jealous, Father Coyote comes up with a plan to show up the Woodpeckers. In the end Father Coyote is embarrassed, and Father Woodpecker explains how you should never pretend to be something you are not.

THE MOTHER MOON

The sun and the moon are honored above all in Pueblo ceremonies. As in many legends, this one is a teaching legend that deals with putting the needs of others before your own. In this Pueblo legend, students learn how day and night came to be. They read how the sun and the moon made the world and how they watch out for their children on earth. Students also learn of Mother-Moon's great sacrifice, which she makes out of love for Father-Sun and their children.

49

TURKEY MAKES CORN AND COYOTE PLANTS IT

The people of the Southwest domesticated turkeys many centuries ago, so they probably considered them friends. In this Apache legend, turkey is a teacher who shows the people how to grow food. He helps the children by giving them food and seeds so they can grow their own food and never want for food again. You may want to discuss that while it was good to feed the children, it was much more valuable for them to learn how to provide for themselves. In this story Coyote is his usual cheating, lazy self. The story gives us insight into why coyotes eat what they can find.

THE COYOTE AND THE BEAR

Coyote is a different character in this Pueblo story than he is in most stories. Usually he is seen as the one who tries to trick others, but here Bear actually tricks Coyote. Coyote is always outsmarted by Bear because he does not think things out. He is always made to look like a fool. The story also shows how some people are only out to help themselves and do not care about the well-being of others.

CROSS-CURRICULAR ACTIVITIES

After students have read these legends, you may wish to have them do some of the following activities.

LANGUAGE ARTS: Explain to the class that a proverb is a short saying that tells a well-known idea or fact, often giving advice. Provide a few examples such as:

✳ An apple a day keeps the doctor away.

✳ Sticks and stones may break my bones, but words will never hurt me.

✳ Beauty is only skin deep.

✳ You can't tell a book by its cover.

Working in groups of four or five, have students brainstorm other proverbs they have heard. Have them list the proverbs on a sheet of paper. Students may also make up their own proverbs that deal with trying to be something you are not or that deal with jealousy. Then have the class share their proverbs. Make a class list of all the proverbs that are similar to Father Woodpecker's wise words.

LANGUAGE ARTS: Read some poems about the moon to the students. Then have students create moon poems of their own. The poems can be about the moon's beauty, shape, size, position in relation to the earth or sun, her usefulness, and so on. Have volunteers share their poems with the rest of the class.

SCIENCE: Discuss with the class the things needed to grow plants such as sun, water, rich soil, fertilizer, and so on. Have students read some books on gardening. Then have each student grow his or her own food plant such as beans, peas, or tomatoes. Start by having students fill three-quarters of a paper cup with soil. Then, after planting the seed, have them chart how long it takes for the plant to sprout, grow secondary leaves, and reach the top of the cup. Once the plant is mature, have students transplant the seedling into a regular size pot and take it home to continue growing. They should make periodic reports on the progress of their plants.

An alternative would be to grow a potato in a cup. A sweet potato or regular potato will do. Have students stick three or four round toothpicks about a quarter of the way into the potato. The toothpicks should be evenly spaced around the sides of the potato; they will hold the potato so it does not fall into the cup. Then place the tip of the potato into a cup that is filled with water. Keep the level of the water near the top, and in a few days, you will see roots starting to grow in the water. Leafy branches will grow from the top of the potato.

ART: Cartoons are useful in getting an idea or point across in very little space. Have students draw a three- or four-panel cartoon that illustrates the main idea or a particular scene from one of the Southwest legends. The legends *Coyote and the Woodpeckers* and *Coyote and the Bear* would be good choices for this exercise. Students should provide the dialogue for their cartoon. Display the cartoons around the room or in another place in the school.

Coyote and the Woodpeckers

Pueblo

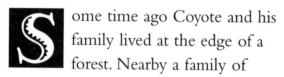

Some time ago Coyote and his family lived at the edge of a forest. Nearby a family of Woodpeckers lived in a big, hollow tree trunk. There were five people in each of the families. One day Father Coyote was strolling through the edge of the forest, and he ran into Father Woodpecker who was taking his morning walk.

"Good evening, Friend Woodpecker," said Father Coyote. "How are you today?"

"I'm doing very well, thank you," replied Father Woodpecker. "And how are you, Friend Coyote?"

Father Coyote answered that he also was doing well, and the two talked for awhile. Just as they were about to part company, Father Coyote said, "Friend Woodpecker, we really should see more of each other. Why don't you and your family come to our house for dinner this evening, and we can get to know each other better."

"I think that is a fine idea," Father Woodpecker said. "We accept your invitation." As you can see, they were both behaving in their most mannerly manner.

That evening Father Woodpecker and his brood went to the Coyotes' house for dinner. Mother Coyote had a very nice meal prepared. Everyone ate with great pleasure. During the meal the Woodpeckers sometimes spread their wings out. When they did this, Father Coyote noticed the red and yellow markings under each wing. After eating, the Woodpeckers again stretched their wings. Father Coyote could again see that they each had lovely colors under their wings.

The Woodpeckers praised the meal highly and remarked about what a good housekeeper Mother Coyote was.

When it was time to go, Coyote walked to the door with the Woodpeckers. Father Woodpecker said, "Thank you for a lovely evening, Friend Coyote. Please allow us to do the same for you, and come to our house tomorrow evening for dinner."

"We would be delighted," Father Coyote replied, and the friends said good-bye.

As soon as the door was closed, Father Coyote turned and said to his wife, "Well, I never!"

"You never what, Dear?" answered Mother Coyote.

"Did you see the airs those Woodpeckers put on?" he continued.

"What airs, Dear?" his wife asked.

"They continually showed off their bright feathers the whole time they were eating dinner! Didn't you notice?"

"I'm afraid I did not," Mother Coyote said.

"Well, I tell you! I want them to know that the Coyotes are equal to the Woodpeckers," he said. "I'll show them!"

The next day Father Coyote told his family to bring him firewood. When he had enough, he lit a very big fire. When it was time for them to go to the Woodpeckers' house for dinner, Father Coyote tied a burning stick under the arms of each of them, with the burning end of the stick pointing toward the front.

"We'll show them, once and for all," he said proudly. "We're really a sight to see!"

And off they went to the Woodpeckers' house. They entered the front door, and a wonderful aroma of cooking food greeted them. While they ate the meal, the Coyotes kept raising their arms to show off the burning coals under them. Father Coyote was very proud, indeed.

But just as they started dessert, one Coyote daughter began screaming. "Father!" she shrieked. "My fire is burning me!"

"Daughter, mind your manners," Coyote told her. "Do not make a fuss about little things!"

Within a few minutes, the other daughter let out a shriek. "Ow!" she cried. "My fire has gone out!"

Father Coyote was very angry. He did not wish his daughters to act this way when they were in the home of others. He told his daughters to be quiet.

"What is the problem, Friend

Coyote?" Father Woodpecker asked, smiling politely. "Why is it that your colors were so bright when you first came here, but now they have become black?"

Trying to smother his anger, Father Coyote said, "Oh, that is the beauty of our colors. Our colors are not always the same like those of others. Ours turn all shades!"

The Coyotes were very uncomfortable, however, because the father could see the half-concealed smirks of the Woodpecker children. Soon he made up excuses, and the Coyotes left to go home. As soon as he entered the front door, Father Coyote punished the children for exposing him to laughter.

"Don't ever shame me like that again!" he shouted.

But in the home of the Woodpeckers, Father Woodpecker gathered his young ones around him and said to them, "Now you see what happens when someone tries to be something they are not. I wish you always to be what you really are, not putting on false colors to show others."

And the little Woodpeckers solemnly nodded their heads in agreement.

"You always know what's best, Dear!" their mother said. ⊡

Questions to Think About

1. Why was Father Coyote jealous?

2. Who was in the wrong at the Woodpeckers' house, Father Coyote or his children? Why?

3. Some stories like Aesop's Fables, have a lesson, or moral. What is the moral of this story?

4. Give an example of how someone might show "false colors" today.

From Lummis, Charles F. *Pueblo Indian Folk-Stories*. University of Nebraska Press, Lincoln and London. Reprint of 1910 version. Originally published in 1894 by the Century Company as *The Man Who Married the Moon*.

The Mother Moon

Pueblo

Long ago when the world was still new, Moon-maiden who dwells above was the loveliest woman in the world. She had no father or mother, nor brother and sister, but she carried within herself the seeds for all of humanity. The Trues, great spirits who made all, created the Sun to be the father of all things. Moon-maiden was meant to be his companion and his wife.

Together, these two made the world and everything in it. They were Father-all and Mother-all and they watched joyfully the happy beings they had created and guarded them against harm. Sun-Father watched them by day, and Moon-Mother watched them by night, shedding their light wherever they went.

Now at this time, Moon-Mother and Sun-Father each had two eyes, so there was no night. Moon-Mother and Sun-Father both shined brightly. The day was filled with golden light, as was the night. Birds flew, and flowers never closed up. The people danced and sang throughout both day and night, never knowing how to rest.

The Trues, who were watching, saw that the world grew tired, and they said to themselves, "This is not good. The people grow weary, and they need rest. We must change the way in which Sun-Father and Moon-Mother light the world. We will put out one of Sun's eyes, so the world will be in darkness half the time. In this way, Sun's children can rest."

When Moon-Mother heard this, she was very unhappy. "Please do not do take the eye of my husband," she said. "Do not blind the eye of Sun, for he provides for our children. He watches to protect them from harm, and he allows them to find game for their food. They could not do that without his light."

The Trues listened well, and at last they said to Moon-Mother, "Very well, we will do as you ask."

Instead they took away one of Moon-Mother's eyes, so she could not see as well. But now there was a night for the tired people. They were able to sleep and find rest. The birds and flowers could rest for a time each day.

Because Moon-Mother had made such a loving sacrifice for her children, she has been able to grow more beautiful as time passes. No wrinkles or age lines for her, and her children love her even more as she grows old. The Trues have been good to her, and she has in her face the beauty found only in the faces of mothers.

So mother-pale above us
she bends her watch to keep,
Who of her sight dear-bought the night
and gives her children sleep.

From Lummis, Charles F. *Pueblo Indian Folk-Stories*. University of Nebraska Press, Lincoln and London, 1992. Reprinted from 1910 edition. Originally published by the Century Company in 1894 as *The Man Who Married the Moon*.

Questions to Think About

1. Why did the Trues feel that a night was necessary?

2. Why do you think Mother-Moon protected Father-Sun from the Trues?

3. How else could the Trues have made night?

4. Would this legend have made sense if Father-Sun had lost the eye? Why?

Turkey Makes Corn and Coyote Plants It

Apache

One day as Turkey was walking along he came across two children, a boy and a girl. The boy was begging the sister for something, and she was saying no.

"What does your little brother want?" Turkey asked the girl.

"He's hungry, but I have no food to give him," she answered.

Turkey felt badly for the children. So using his magical powers, he shook himself all over. As he shook, many different kinds of wild foods and seeds fell out of his body. The boy and girl quickly picked up the wonderful food and ate it, for they had had nothing for days.

Turkey shook himself again. This time different kinds of corn fell from his body. "There are different kinds of corn

for you," he said.

He shook himself again, and yellow corn dropped. "There is yellow corn for you," he said.

He shook himself a fourth time, and white corn fell from his body. "And there is white corn for you," he said. The happy children gathered it all up.

"Now we need to get to work," Turkey said to the brother and sister. "I have given you four different kinds of corn seeds, and this is a good place to plant them."

The boy and girl cut digging sticks and began making holes with them. They dug many holes, and into each one they put corn seeds. The corn was growing by the next day and already was a foot and a half high. "This is good," the sister said. "Now we must plant the squash seeds."

After they planted the squash seeds they said to Turkey, "Our corn is growing well. We want to make another garden and plant more corn."

Turkey thought that was a good idea, and he gave them some more seeds. The brother and sister went to work in the fields and planted more corn.

One day they heard Turkey hollering in the field, and they went out to see what was the matter. Turkey was dragging one wing along the ground, and there were snakes on the other side of him.

"What are you doing?" the sister asked.

"I am trying to lure the snakes away from you," he told them.

By now the squash plants had many squash on them, and the corn was tall and wore tassels full of pollen at their tops. The snakes had been trying to get the pollen from the corn tassels.

"Stay away from the corn plants for four days," Turkey told the children. "When you come back, the snakes will be through gathering their pollen and the corn will be ripe."

When the brother and sister returned four days later, the corn was ripe. "This is the only time the corn will ripen in four days," Turkey said. "After this, it will take much longer." And he was right.

After a while, the brother and sister shared some seeds with other people. Slim Coyote came to them. "I would like to have some corn seeds, too," he said. "I want to plant them for myself."

The brother and sister wondered about this, because they knew that Coyote does not like to work, but they gave him some seeds, anyway.

"Thanks a lot," Coyote said. "I know a better way to plant corn than these other people do."

"Oh, what is that?" the sister asked.

"Well, these other people plant their corn, and after it's grown, they have to cook it. That's not the way I'm going to do it," he told her. "I'm going to cook my corn first, then after it's ripe, I won't have to cook it again!"

And that's what he did. He cooked his corn and ate some of it. Then he planted the rest and sat back to wait for it to grow.

"You people don't know how to do things right," he boasted. "When my corn grows, it will already be cooked!"

The brother and sister looked at him wide-mouthed for a moment. Then they went about their business, while Coyote went to gather acorns. When they returned to the fields, all the corn was growing, except Coyote's.

"You people took the hearts out of my corn before you gave the seeds to me," Coyote accused the children.

"No, we didn't," they answered. "You cooked the hearts out of them yourself when you cooked them."

Coyote didn't like to admit he was wrong, and he said, "Give me some more corn seeds. I'm going to try again."

This time he planted the corn the right way. The next day his corn was a foot and a half high. The other people were harvesting their corn by now and were gathering it into big bundles. When Coyote saw what they were doing, he wanted some of their corn.

"Give me some of your corn," he said. "My children are hungry. Mine is not ready yet. I'll pay you back."

"Coyote, you're always asking us for corn," the people said. They were angry at Coyote because he always tried to get whatever they had. "Go away! Get your own corn!"

So Coyote waited until no one was looking, and he stole some of the squash that was still growing in the gardens. The people all came to where he lived and said, "Are you the one who's been stealing our squash?"

"Every time anything bad happens around here you always blame me," Coyote said pouting. "You always blame me for stealing. There are lots of other people around here who could have stolen it. Don't come looking for me!"

But the people knew that Coyote was a thief. "Go away from here, and don't come back," they told him. "Go live somewhere else!"

"Well!" Coyote said indignantly. "I was going to pay you back for the corn you gave me, but I don't like the way you have treated me, so I'm not going to now! I'll show you!"

And he stomped away, taking his family with him. But Coyote and his family never had very much to eat, and what they had, they didn't even cook before they ate it. And that's the way Coyote was. □

From Erdoes, Richard and Alfonso, Ortiz. *American Indian Myths and Legends.* Pantheon Books, New York, 1984. Originally from Goodwin, Grenville. *Memoirs of the American Folklore Society,* Vol. 33, copyright 1939 by the American Folklore Society.

Questions to Think About

1. *From whom did the children get the seeds?*

2. *Why did the people ask Coyote to leave? What would you have done?*

3. *Do you think the people had the right to tell Coyote to go away? Why?*

4. *Is there a moral to this story? What do think it is?*

The Coyote and the Bear

Pueblo

One day Bear and Coyote happened to meet and sat together to visit awhile. Bear said to Coyote, "Friend Coyote, look at this good land on which we sit. Why don't we farm it together and share what we grow?"

"That is a very good idea," Coyote replied. "What shall we plant?"

"I think we should plant potatoes," Bear said, "and there is a very good way for us to divide them up when they are grown."

"Potatoes sound good," Coyote agreed. "How should we divide them?"

"Well, Friend Coyote, I shall take everything that grows under the ground, and you can take everything that grows above the ground," Bear offered. "In that way, when the crop is grown, each of us can take his part of the harvest without any disagreement."

Coyote did not think much before he replied. "That sounds like an excellent idea, Friend Bear," he said at last.

And so that is what they planned to do. They plowed the ground with sharp sticks and planted their potatoes. They worked together all through the summer, chopping weeds with stone hoes and watering the plants from the irrigation ditch. At harvest time Coyote cut off all the tops of the plants and took them home, while Bear dug up all the potatoes.

Coyote looked at the drying potato plant leaves and stems that he had taken for himself, and then at the nice, round, fat potatoes Bear had for his share of the crop.

"This is not fair," he said. "You now have all the good parts to eat, and the parts that I have are good for nothing. My wife and I will starve."

Bear reminded him, "We had an agreement. Do you now not wish to stick to the pact we made?"

Coyote was very unhappy, so he went home with his tail dragging.

The next spring, however, when Bear came to him again, he smiled as Bear said, "Friend Coyote, I would like to plant the ground with you again. But because you were so unhappy with the last crop we planted, why don't we plant corn instead? This time, you can have all the crop that lies beneath the ground, and I will take the part that is above the ground."

"That sounds like a good idea to me," Coyote said, and so they started to work.

They plowed the ground with sharp pointed sticks and planted kernels of corn. They worked together all through the summer, chopping the weeds with stone hoes and watering the plants from the irrigation ditch. When time came to harvest the corn, Bear gathered up all the stalks and ears of corn, and Coyote dug up his share. But Coyote found nothing except thin, thready roots that could feed nothing.

Coyote was very unhappy and said to Bear, "Friend Bear, this is not fair. You have gotten all the good parts to eat, while my wife and I get nothing. We will starve."

Bear reminded him, "Friend Coyote, this is what we agreed upon. Are you now going to go back on your promise?" Coyote slunk away.

That winter Coyote and his wife were very hungry. Coyote was walking along the frozen river one day when he saw Bear sitting on the ice eating a fish. The fish smelled very good to Coyote, who had had nothing to eat for days. Coyote said, "Friend Bear, where did you get that wonderful fish that smells so good?"

"I broke a hole in the ice and fished for it," Bear replied. "This river is full of them," and he continued eating the fish.

"Will you show me how to catch them?" Coyote asked. Smelling the fish, Coyote was close to fainting from hunger as he watched Bear eating.

"Of course," answered Bear, "it is very easy. All you do is break a hole in the ice, then sit with your tail hanging into the water. When you feel a nibble, however, do not pull up your tail until I tell you to do so."

Bear broke a hole in the ice, and Coyote sat down on the ice with his tail hanging through the hole. Ice began to freeze around his tail, and he said, "Friend Bear, I feel a nibble. Let me pull up my tail."

"Oh, no, not yet," Bear told him. "Wait until your fish has a good hold on your tail, so you will not lose him."

Coyote waited, and soon his tail was frozen in the ice. He tried and tried with all his might, but he could not get his tail out of the ice.

"Ouch! It hurts," he cried, and Bear doubled over with laughter.

"Ha, ha, ha," Bear laughed and rolled on the ice until his sides hurt from laughing so much. Then he took his last fish and started toward home, occasionally looking back over his shoulder at Coyote and laughing again.

Coyote was stuck in the ice. He could not get out of the ice until a thaw came, which was days later. When he was finally able to get free from the ice, Coyote was wet and cold and nearly starved. From that day on, he has never forgiven Bear. When they meet, Bear always smiles and says politely, "Good morning, Friend Coyote," or "Good afternoon, Friend Coyote."

But Coyote will not speak to Bear or even look at him, because Bear played such a mean trick on Coyote. ▫

Questions to Think About

1. Why is Coyote mad at Bear?

2. Why did Coyote always get the bad end of the deal? Does this ever happen to you? How does it make you feel?

3. What lesson should Coyote have learned from his dealings with Bear?

4. Do you think Coyote was ever tricked by Bear again? Why?

From Lummis, Charles F. *Pueblo Indian Folk Stories.* University of Nebraska Press, 1992. Reprint of the 1910 edition. Originally published by the Century Company in 1984 as *The Man Who Married the Moon.*

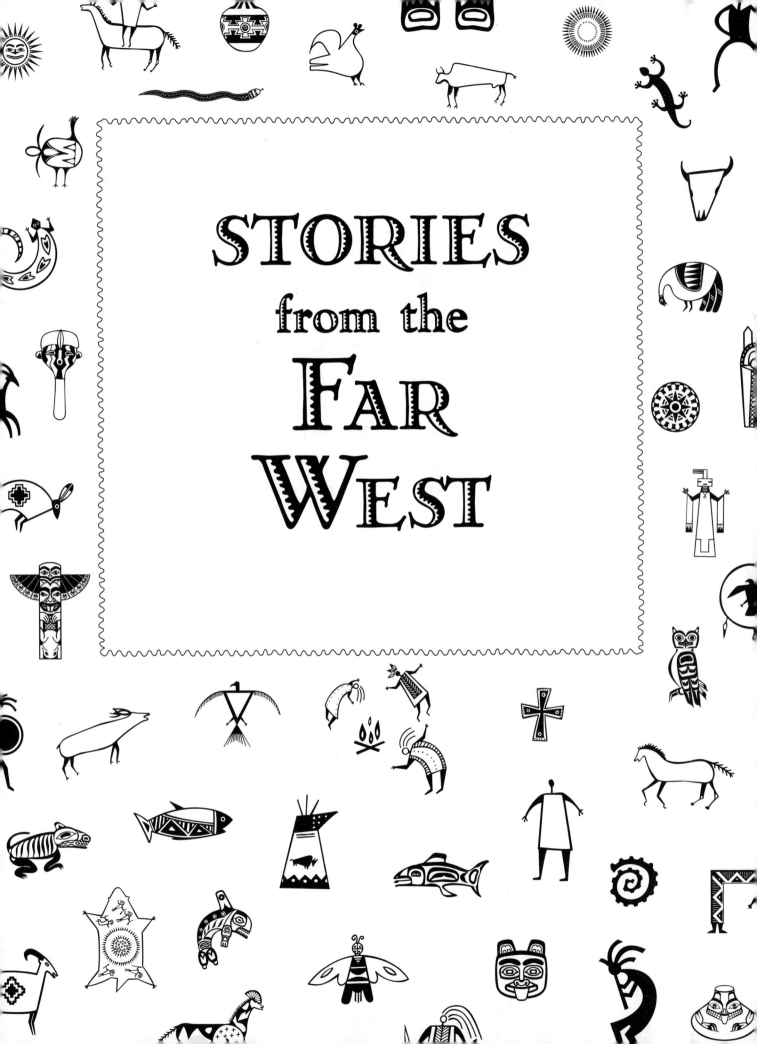

STORIES
from the
FAR
WEST

STORIES from the FAR WEST

The Origin of the Sierra Nevada and the Coast Range (Yokut)

Coyote Makes First Man (Miwok)

How Robin Got His Red Breast (Miwok)

The Native Americans of California included the Pomo, Wintun, Chumash, Klamath, Modoc, Yurok, Patwin, Maida, Miwok, and Yokut, to name a few. The Miwok, who lived mostly in central California, were one of the largest Native American groups in California. The Native Americans of California lived in small bands and villages scattered throughout what is now California. Mostly docile and peaceful, the Native Americans in California spoke over 100 different languages. These people were hunters, fishermen, and gatherers of wild foods such as seeds, nuts, and acorns. Due to the mild weather, clothing was minimal in this region.

The arriving Spaniards, the first Europeans to venture into California, met little resistance from the Native Americans. Except for the Spaniards and a few Russians, the Californian Native Americans saw very little of Europeans until the onset of the Gold Rush in 1849. When settlers finally did come to California, however, their coming was overwhelmingly destructive. Some Native Americans drifted away from the area when settlers came. Some died from epidemics caused by diseases the settlers brought, and others were killed by the gold miners. Many Native American groups in this region were wiped out within a few decades of the arrival of the new settlers.

Like stories from other regions, those that have been recorded from the far West involve animals and Native Americans. Similarly, the Coyote also appears in stories from this region, usually as a trickster. Coyote appears in the legends in this section. He is a creator in a Miwok legend. The other two stories in this section are centered around birds. The robin in the Miwok story brings people fire, while the Crow and Hawk make mountains in the Yokut legend.

All of the stories in this section deal with how things came to be, man, fire, and mountains. Each Native American group has its own versions of how these things came to be; some are very similar. As you read these legends, try to remember other legends you have read that are similar to these. The following is a brief synopsis of each legend in this section.

ORIGIN OF THE SIERRA NEVADA AND THE COAST RANGE

Animals had much power in Native American legends. The birds are the animals with power in this legend. Their power was so great, that they were able to make mountains and move them. In this Yokut legend, Crow and Hawk create the Sierra Nevada and Coast Range. Crow builds higher mountains than Hawk. This so angers Hawk he rotates the mountains so that the mountains on his side are higher. After reading this legend, you may want to have students use a map to locate the places mentioned.

COYOTE MAKES FIRST MAN

Coyote is a changing character in Native American legends; sometimes he is a trickster and sometimes he is a creator. In this humorous Miwok story, the animals discuss what man should look like. Each animal wants man to look like him or herself. Coyote has his own idea of how man should look. Being the slyest, Coyote waits until the other animals are asleep, and then he gives man life.

HOW ROBIN GOT HIS RED BREAST

This is a story about how fire was stolen, but it is also a story about robins. In this Miwok legend, Robin steals fire and uses his breast to keep the fire from going out. This burned his breast, leaving it forever red. In this story we learn that by rubbing two sticks together we can make fire. This is an example of the Native American belief that fire is contained naturally within the wood.

CROSS-CURRICULAR ACTIVITIES

After students have read these legends, you may wish to have them do some of the following activities.

SOCIAL STUDIES: Although *Origin of the Sierra Nevada and the Coast Range* is a legend, the story deals with real places. Have students look up California on a map or in an atlas and find the two mountain ranges mentioned in this story. Help them to locate Tulare Lake, Tehachapi Pass, and Mount Shasta. Then have them answer the following questions: How high is Mount Shasta? (14,162 feet) What is the elevation of Tehachapi Pass? (3,793 feet) What is the tallest mountain in California? (Mt. Whitney, 14,494 feet) In which mountain range is that mountain? (Sierra Nevada) Why is the Coast Range called by that name? (Because of its close proximity to the coastline.) Go over the answers as a class.

SCIENCE: People have long been interested in the beautiful creatures we call "birds of prey." Tell students that in addition to many kinds of hawks, birds of prey include eagles, falcons, vultures, and condors. Point out that the Native American was especially awed by the eagle, because when it soars through the air, it is extremely beautiful. Many Native American groups prized the wing feathers from the eagle. They believed that wearing one or more of these feathers in the hair would give some of the eagle's power to the one wearing it. See if anyone knows the national bird of the United States (bald eagle). Now have students research one of the birds of prey. When they have learned about it, have them report back to the class. Have students take turns telling their classmates what they have learned. If you wish, students may work in small groups to prepare presentations.

ART: Discuss with students how they would have designed people if they had created the world. Make a list of all the characteristics they think the ideal person should have. Then have each student write a description of what the person would look like. Next, have students use clay to model their person or draw a picture to illustrate their description. Display finished projects under the heading "What Man Might Have Been."

LANGUAGE ARTS: There are many

stories about how the world and the first people came to be. Have students research at least three legends about how the beginning of the world or the first people came to be. A good source of stories is *In the Beginning* by Virginia Hamilton, which is a collection of creation stories from around the world, or you could have students find their own source. Have students choose the story they like best. After they practice, have students retell the legend they like to the class. Discuss the similarities and differences among all the legends and how they compare to *Coyote Makes First Man* and *Origin of the Sierra Nevada* and *the Coast Range*.

SCIENCE: Using modeling clay, anchor three candles upright in three saucers or jar lids. Place them in a safe place on a counter or table and light them. Leave one candle uncovered. Place a small jar over one candle and a large jar over the third candle. Now have students guess which candle will burn the longest. Discuss the reasons for their choices. At the end of the experiment only the uncovered candle will be burning. Explain, or see if students can explain, that fire will not burn without oxygen. The candle that is not covered gets all the oxygen it needs and therefore burns. The candle in the small jar runs out of oxygen quickly and goes out. The candle in the large jar burns longer because it has more oxygen than the one in the small jar.

LANGUAGE ARTS: Have students create a poem telling how robin got his red breast. They can use the Miwok legend as a guide for their poem or create one based on their own idea of how robin got his red breast. Another option is to have students write a poem about how fire came to be. Have students share their poems with the rest of the class.

Origin of the Sierra Nevada and the Coast Range

Yokut

In the beginning, there was only water on the earth and Hawk and Crow. Near the place that is now Tulare Lake (approximately 50 miles south of Fresno, California) stood a pole on which these two sat. They spent their time knocking each other off the pole. First Hawk would knock off Crow, and then Crow would knock off Hawk. They kept this up for many ages. After a while they grew tired of this game, so they created Kingfisher, Eagle, Pelican, Duck, and many others.

Duck was a small bird. One time, she dived to the bottom of the water and took a small amount of mud from the bottom. Duck had gone so deep, however, that by the time she got back to the surface of the water, she had died. She floated to the top where Hawk and Crow saw her. They took the mud from Duck's beak and started making mountains.

They started at Tehachapi Pass (north of Los Angeles), with Hawk making the eastern ridge and Crow the western ridge. They pushed the mud down deep into the water, then piled it high on top, working toward the north. Finally they finished up together at Mount

Shasta (in northern California).

Hawk looked at the mountains Crow had made and said, "What have you done, you rascal? You have taken some of my earth and made your mountains bigger!"

Crow laughed, because he had tricked Hawk.

Hawk sat down and chewed some Indian tobacco, which made him think hard. At once, he grabbed the mountains and rotated them around in a circle. So now the mountains Crow had made were to the east, and the ones Crow had made were to the west. And that is how the Sierras came to be bigger than the Coast Range. ⊡

From Judson, Katherine Berry. *Myths and Legends of California and the Old Southwest.* A. C. McClurg & Co., 1912.

Questions to Think About

1. According to the Yokut legend, how did the Sierra Nevada and Coast Range come to be? Do some research to find out the way scientists explain it.

2. Why is one mountain range higher than the other?

3. Why do you think Crow made his mountains higher?

4. Do you think Crow cared that Hawk switched the mountains around? Why?

Coyote Makes First Man

Miwok

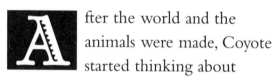

After the world and the animals were made, Coyote started thinking about making First Man. He called a council of all the animals. When the animals arrived at the council site in the forest, they sat in a circle, just as Native Americans do. Lion sat at the head of the circle. To his right was Grizzly Bear, then pretty little Cinnamon Bear, and on around the circle to Mouse, who sat at Lion's left.

Lion, as the Head Chief of all the animals, spoke first. "I wish First Man to have a large voice, like mine," he said. "That way, he could frighten all the other animals with his voice. I also think he should be covered with hair and have long claws and strong teeth."

Grizzly Bear laughed at Lion's idea. "If First Man was given a loud voice such as Lion's," he said, "he would frighten away all the game for which he was hunting. I think he should be very strong. Also, he should be able to move silently and swiftly so he can seize his prey without noise."

Deer Stag said, "I think a loud voice for First Man would be absurd, but he should have ears like a spider's web and eyes like fire. And he absolutely must have antlers for protection."

"Oh no!" Mountain Sheep said. "Branching antlers would be a hazard for First Man. They would get caught in the thickets and prevent him from moving about. First Man needs to have horns that are hard as stone and horns rolled up to the side of his head. These would give his head weight with which to butt very hard."

Coyote thought all of the ideas spoken were foolish, and it was obvious that each of these animals wanted First Man to be just like each of them.

"I can make a man who is even better looking than I am," he bragged. "He would have four legs with five fingers on each leg. He would have a strong voice, but not roar all the time. He would have feet like Grizzly's, because then he would be able to stand erect when he needed to. But he would not have a tail like Grizzly. Man would have good eyes and ears like Deer Stag. Hair is a burden to have during warm weather, so Man should not be covered with fur. He would have claws like Eagle's, and, of course, he would have my wit and intelligence!" Very pleased with himself and his idea of First Man, Coyote sat down.

Beaver talked next. "First Man must have a tail," she said, "a broad, flat one. With such a tail he could carry mud and sand. But he should not have a furry tail, because that would attract fleas."

The animals continued to add their ideas about what First Man should look like, and sometimes they argued. Owl said Man needed wings, but Mole said that would be silly because he would only bump against the sky. Besides, if he had both wings and eyes, he would burn his eyes flying too close to the sun. Without eyes, he could burrow in the soft, cool earth and be happy there.

Mouse disagreed, however. "Who wants to dig through the earth all the time? Man would need eyes to see what he was eating," she said.

Every animal at the council wanted First Man to be like him or her, so each, except Coyote, took a lump of clay and began to model it to look just like themselves. Coyote, however, took his lump of clay and started molding a man that looked just like the man he had described to the council.

The animals had spent so much time arguing that it soon got late, and the animals began to get sleepy. One by one the animals began to fall asleep before they had finished their models. Coyote, however, was cunning and stayed awake. He worked hard into the night on his model. After the other animals fell asleep, he threw water on their lumps of clay, which spoiled them.

In the morning coyote finished his model and gave it life. And this is how Coyote made First Man. ▫

From Judson, Katherine Berry. *Myths and Legends of California and the Old Southwest.* A. C. McClurg & Co., 1912.

Questions to Think About

1. *Who created Man in this legend? Why do you think so many cultures have legends like this?*

2. *Why do you think the other animals wanted Man to look like each of them?*

3. *Why do you think Coyote chose not to have Man look like him?*

How Robin Got His Red Breast

Miwok

Before the world was finished, it was still dark and cold. The people had no fire. Robin learned where the fire was and set out upon a long journey to get it for the people. He traveled a very long way before he at last found the fire and stole it.

Since the journey was a very long one, it took Robin many days to make it. Every night on his way home, Robin would lay with his breast over the fire to keep it from going out. Being so close to the fire turned his breast red.

Finally he reached home with the fire for the people. Robin made the Sun out of fire. Before doing this, however, he put some of the fire inside the buckeye tree, so the people could get fire when they needed it. Since that time the people have known that to get fire they must rub a stick of the buckeye tree against a piece of dry wood, and this makes the fire come out. ▫

From Merriam, C. Hart. *The Dawn of the World*. The Arthur H. Clark Company, 1910.

Questions to Think About

1. *How did the Robin get his red Breast?*

2. *Is there any truth in this story?*

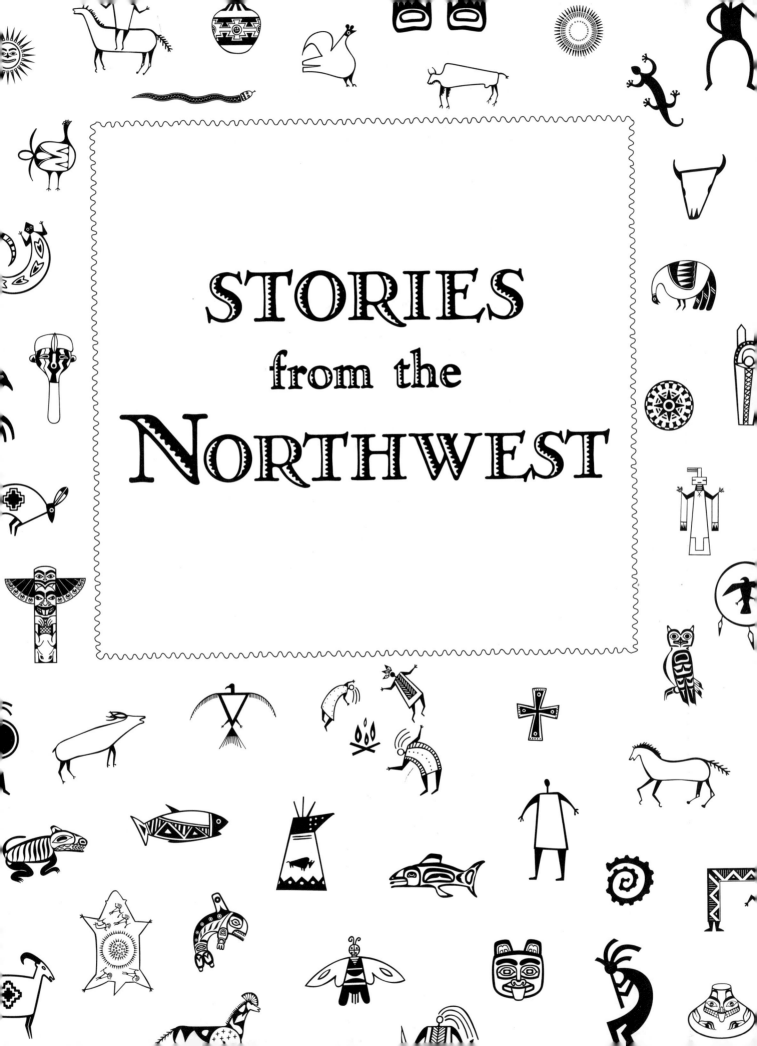

STORIES from the NORTHWEST

STORIES from the NORTHWEST

Pushing Up the Sky (Snohomish)

Wakiash and the First Totem Pole (Kwakiutl)

The Great Canoe in the Sky (Salish)

The Animals Climb into the Sky (Kootenay)

The Origin of Cedar Trees (Haida)

The Punishment of the Stingy (Chinook)

The Native Americans who once inhabited present-day Oregon, Washington, and the coast of British Columbia, Canada, included the Tlingit, Haida, Salish, Snohomish, Chinook, and Kwakiutl, to name a few. Due to their close proximity to the sea, these people relied on the sea for food rather than on agriculture. They also hunted. Most villages or towns were located right on the coast. Because the area was a densely populated region, warfare occurred frequently.

The northwest region is a beautiful country rich in natural resources. When the Europeans came to North America, the Native Americans of this land lived comfortable lives. They had no metal tools at that time, only stone tools. Yet they were able to construct large, weathertight houses and boats big enough to carry as many as 40 or 50 people. Some of these boats were used in hunting the great whales.

The cedar tree was almost as important to these people as the buffalo was to the people of the Plains. With great redwood, Douglas Fir, and pine forests in the area, wood was abundant. Unlike other Native American groups you have read about, these people built solid permanent wooden homes with thick beams and planks. Usually several families could occupy one large house.

The wood was also used to build their strong canoes, something very important to these sea-going communities. From the trees they also obtained wood to make clothing and cooking containers. Watertight boxes covered in painted or carved designs were made for storage and for cooking. The wood of the cedar was also made into totem poles, often many feet tall; ceremonial masks; drums; and eating utensils. They even made a kind of fabric for clothing from the bark of the tree.

Two stories in this section reflect the importance of wood in this region. In *The Origin of Cedar Trees*, we learn how the great red cedar trees came to be. In the other story, *Wakiash and the First Totem Pole,* we learn how totem poles came to be. Totem poles are very important to many of the groups in the Northwest.

People tell stories about what is most important to them, so it is not surprising that many of the stories of the Northwest are about fish, wildlife, and the cedar tree. As was true with other Native American groups, the plants, animals, and heavenly bodies were thought to have once been human, so many stories were told about these things. Three stories in this section deal with the sky and stars: *The Great Canoe in the Sky, The Animals Climb into the Sky, and Pushing Up the Sky.* Another

story, *The Punishment of the Stingy*, deals with how people are punished for selfish behavior. The following is a brief synopsis of each of the legends in this section.

PUSHING UP THE SKY

This Snohomish tale was told to show people how much they could accomplish by working together. It points out that even though people speak different languages, they can still find a way to work together to accomplish a common goal. The story also illustrates the belief that all the stars with names were once humans or animals living on earth.

WAKIASH AND THE FIRST TOTEM POLE

This Kwakiutl story explains the legendary origin of the totem pole. The totem pole served much the same purpose for the Native American of the Northwest as the family crest did for the European nobility. The totem of a family showed the legendary descent of a family or clan from an animal such as the beaver, raven, or eagle. They did not worship this animal but took the animal as a symbol for the family or clan. The totem served a practical purpose, for when a person traveled from one village to another, he or she had only to look for a house with his totem in front, and he or she would be sure to have a place to stay for the night.

THE GREAT CANOE IN THE SKY

Bluejay and Old Man Coyote are friends to humans in this story. Old Man Coyote is the venerable elder to whom other animals go to for help. In this Salish legend, we find out how Old Man Coyote saves five fishermen friends from drowning by putting them and their canoe up in the sky. Boats were extremely important to the Salish because they were fishermen who relied on fish as the mainstay of their diet. They built wonderful boats from the trunks of trees, which they hollowed out with fire and tools made of stone.

THE ANIMALS CLIMB INTO THE SKY

In this Kootenay legend, the animals visit the Sky People and are stranded there when Glutton pulls the rope down. We then learn how the Rocky Mountains came to be, how birds got their feathers, why there are fish and land animals, and how some stars came to be. The Okanagon and the Shusway versions of this story are almost the same as this one. In some versions Chickadees, Wrens, Woodpeckers, or Sapsuckers take the role of the Hawks in this story.

THE ORIGIN OF CEDAR TREES

This story takes place in the Queen Charlotte Islands off the coast of British Columbia, Canada. It tells the story of how selfishness, jealousy, greed, and other evil ways were not tolerated by the Creator. In this Haida tale, destructive behavior is turned into constructive behavior, and the result is the creation of beauty—the cedar trees.

THE PUNISHMENT OF THE STINGY

In this Chinook story, Bluejay is the villain and Raven, who usually is the trickster in stories, is the one who tries to help the community. This story tells how hunters go out looking for food, which they find but do not share with the rest of the villagers. The Chief's son always tries to go with the hunters but is always turned away. Finally, the boy dons an eagle's skin and flies out to where the hunters are. Seeing what they have been up to, he turns their families into killer whales and birds, leaving the hunters all alone. Like other Native American legends, this one teaches an important lesson: people who are stingy will be punished eventually.

CROSS-CURRICULAR ACTIVITIES

After students have read these legends, you may wish to have them do some of the following activities.

SOCIAL STUDIES: After reading *Pushing Up the Sky*, explain to students that there were once over 300 groups of Native Americans speaking probably 2,000 or more languages and dialects. Add to this the number of languages all the different immigrant groups brought to North America, and you will find it almost impossible to calculate the number of languages spoken here. Explain to the students the meaning of *immigrant* (people who came here from another country). Ask students how many know people who have come here from other countries. Then have students investigate their own ethnic or national backgrounds. They can start by asking their parents or grandparents the following questions: In what country was I born? In what country were you (parent) born? What language did you speak as a child? Where were your parents (students' grandparents) born? What language did they speak as children? From which different countries did your ancestors come? (Have students go back as far as they have to to find an ancestor who came from another country.) Do you know how many years your ancestors have lived here? After students have gotten answers to these questions, create a class bar graph to show how many students were born in the U.S., how many were born somewhere else, how many have one parent born here, how many have one parent born someplace else, and so on. Discuss the results of your graph.

ART: The Northwest Indians were not the only people ever to have considered a certain animal as standing for their family. Ask students if any of them have a family crest. You may want to bring in a book that shows samples of European crests. Have students create a crest for their family. They should begin by thinking of an animal that might represent their family. Suggest a lion for courage and strength, an ant for hardiness and diligence, a bear for ferocity, a fox for slyness, a beaver for industry, and so on. After students have chosen the animal, have them design a family crest based on that animal. They can add any other items they would like to the crest. Students could create a crest or a totem pole. Students who wish to create totem poles can draw them or carve them into a bar of soap with a craft knife.

MATH: Students learned about the great cedar trees in *The Origin of Cedar Trees*. Tell students that they can estimate the height of a tree without actually measuring it. Divide the students into pairs for this activity and pick several nearby trees for them to measure. Have one student measure out about 60 feet from a chosen tree. Then hold a yardstick upright at this point. The second person should lie flat on the ground about six feet behind the first person. Then the second person should look up to where the top of the tree comes into his or her vision on the stick. The partner can mark the spot on the stick by having him or her move a hand down on the stick as you direct them. Then have the pair multiply the number of inches they measured on the stick by ten; this will give them the estimated height of the tree.

SCIENCE: In *The Origin of Cedar Trees*, students learned about the different uses Native Americans had for cedar trees. Have students create a list of things we use today that come from trees. They can start by looking around their homes, the school, the neighborhood, and even in the refrigerator. Then have students bring their list to class to share with their classmates. If you wish, students could make posters showing the information they have found. Discuss students' findings.

SCIENCE: Some students may be interested in studying killer whales after reading *The Punishment of the Stingy*. Killer whales are often important characters in the stories of the Northwest fishers. These animals are very beautiful with their large black and pure white coloring. Have students research the whale to learn about its habitat, enemies, feeding sources, and whether or not it is an endangered animal. Then have them create a poster showing the whale and the most important information they found. Others may wish to create a diorama that illustrates what they have learned about the life of killer whales. Display the finished projects in your classroom.

Pushing Up the Sky

Snohomish

When the Creator first made the world and the people, he began in the East, gradually moving westward as he worked. As he worked his way west, he scattered the people all over the land. He divided up the languages he had, giving different languages to different people. When he reached Puget Sound, he decided to go no further because he liked it there so much. He still had many languages left, though, so he gave out all of the remaining languages to the people in that area. This is why there are so many Native American languages. This is also the reason why the peoples of different places were unable to talk to each other in the early days.

The Creator had made one very big mistake when he made the world; he had hung the sky too low. The tall people were always bumping their heads against it, and some people would do what was forbidden by climbing the tall trees and entering into the Sky World.

Everyone knew that the sky needed to be pushed up. It would take all the people to move the sky. But how could all the people with their different languages accomplish such a task?

The wise men of each group got together for a big council to decide what to do about the sky.

One elder said, "I know we can raise the sky, if all of us work together, but we'll need both people and animals working together to do it."

"But how can we do that?" asked another. "We all live in different places and we speak different languages. How can we all manage to push at the same time?"

The wise men had talked and talked for many hours, puzzling over the problem. Finally, someone came up with a solution. "We will have a signal that everyone can recognize," he said. "There is one saying that means the same in all our languages. *Ya-hoh* means 'lift together' for all of us. When the time comes to push up the sky, one of us will shout *Ya-hoh* for all to hear, and everyone will know that is the signal to push."

So it was agreed. All the peoples made poles of the tallest giant fir trees, and on the day that had been decided was best for the sky-raising, they waited for the signal.

The leader with the loudest and clearest voice shouted, "Ya-hoooh!" and on the *hoooh* the people pushed with all their might. The sky moved up a few inches. The call went out a second time, "Ya-hoooh!" and everyone pushed again. Several times the call went out until, finally, the sky was raised to where it now hangs. Since that time, no one has bumped his or her head on the sky, and no one has been able to climb into the Sky World.

Now, while the people were pushing up the sky, three hunters had been chasing four elk. At exactly the same time as the people began their pushing, the elk and hunters were at that very spot where the sky joins the world. When the signal, *Ya-hoooh*, was sounded, the elk ran up into the Sky World with the hunters running close after them. Now they too were lifted, just as the sky was.

The hunters and elk became stars. Today you can see the hunters forming the handle of the Big Dipper, and the four elks forming its bowl. Some other people were raised up into the Sky World, as well, and up there in each of two canoes you can see three men. You can also see a fish in the Sky World.

These human and animal people were once alive on earth, but now they must remain above as star people.

Today we still shout "Ya-hoh!" when we are working together or trying to lift something heavy. When we do this, we use all our energy, especially on the very last part of the signal, so it comes out, "Ya-hoooooh!" And when we say it this way together, we know we can raise the sky. ▫

From Clark, Ella E. *Indian Legends of the Pacific Northwest*. University of California Press, 1953.

Questions to Think About

1. *Why was it difficult for the people to work together?*

2. *Besides raising the sky, what else of importance happened in this story?*

3. *What do you think the point of this story is?*

Wakiash and the First Totem Pole

Kwakiutl

akiash was a good chief. He was generous and open-handed with gifts and therefore highly regarded by his people. He had never created a dance of his own, however, and for this he felt bad. You see, he was the only chief without his own dance. So one day he thought, "I will go into the mountains and fast and hope for a vision. Maybe in my vision a dance will come to me."

So Wakiash went to the mountains. He fasted for four days and prayed for a vision. He did not eat or drink for all this time. On the fourth day, he was very tired, so he lay down to rest. While he was lying there, he fell asleep. When he woke, he found a frog lying on his chest.

"Lie still," the frog told him. "We are on the back of a raven, and he is going to fly around the world. You will be able to see everything on earth, and when you see what you want, you can take it."

The raven flew for four days with Wakiash on his back. Wakiash lay forward, and from his great height he saw many things. On the way back, he spotted a house that had a beautiful totem pole in front. He could hear the sound of singing coming from the house, and thinking these things were good, he thought, "I would like to take those things home with me."

The frog knew the thoughts of Wakiash, and he told the raven to stop. They coasted to the ground, and the frog said to Wakiash, "Now hide behind the door of the house. Stay right here, and when the people begin to dance, leap into the room."

Wakiash did as the frog told him, but something happened inside the house. The people stopped dancing. Their chief said, "Something is wrong. Someone must be near us who is making us feel bad, so we can't dance. We need someone to run quickly around the house and find out what is wrong."

"I will go," said a little mouse. "I can creep anywhere, even into a box, and if anyone is hiding, I will find him."

You see, all the people in the house were really animals who had taken off their animal clothing for the dance. The little mouse too had taken off her mouse skin clothing so she looked like a woman.

Now the mouse put on her mouse clothing and ran outside the house. Wakiash caught her and said, "Ha! I have a gift for you, my friend." He gave her a piece of fat from a mountain goat, which was something she really enjoyed.

Pleased with the gift Wakiash had given her, the mouse said, "What is it you want? How can I help you?"

"I want the totem pole, the house, and the dances and songs that go with them," he answered.

"Stay right here," the mouse said. "Wait until I return."

Wakiash waited outside while the mouse went back in and told the people, "I have looked everywhere, but I can find no one."

The chief, who was really a beaver when he was wearing his animal clothing, said, "Let's try again to dance."

Three times they tried, but they could not dance. Each time they tried, they sent the mouse out again to look, but each time she only chatted with Wakiash and then went back inside to report there was no one outside.

Finally the people began to dance. Then Wakiash sprang inside the house. The people all stopped dancing and dropped their heads in shame. You see they did not want a human to see them looking like people, when they were really animals.

They stood without speaking until one said, at last, "Let's not waste time. Let's ask our friend here what he wants." They lifted up their heads.

"What is it you want?" the chief asked.

"I would like to have your dance because I have never had one of my own," Wakiash said. "I also would like to have your house and the totem pole that stands in front of your door," Wakiash thought.

He did not have to speak because the mouse could read his thoughts, and she told the people what Wakiash wanted.

The chief said, "Sit down, friend. We will show you our dances, and you can pick out the one you want."

The people began to dance again. When they finished, the chief said, "Which dance would you like?"

Wakiash had been watching closely. The dancers wore masks as they danced. Wakiash had especially liked the Echo mask and the mask of the Little Man who always walks around the house trying to start arguments. He formed his wishes in his mind, and the mouse told the chief, "Our friend would like the Echo dance and the Little Man dance."

The people began to dance again and taught the dances to Wakiash. Then the chief said, "You may take as many dances and masks as you wish, and you may also have the totem pole."

He told Wakiash that when he returned home, these things would go with him, and he could use all of them in one dance. He also said, "From now on, your name will be Kalakuyuwish, which means sky pole, because the totem pole is so tall."

The chief folded the house up into a little bundle and gave it to Wakiash with a headdress and said, "When you reach your home, throw down this bundle. The house will become as it was when you first saw it, and then you will be able to give a dance."

Wakiash climbed back onto the raven. They flew away toward the mountain from which they had come. Wakiash fell asleep on the raven's back, for he was very tired. When he awoke, it was night, and the raven and the frog were gone. But he still had the bundle that had been given to him by the animal people.

He threw down the bundle, and the house with the totem pole appeared. A great whale was painted on the side of the house, and it was blowing through its blow hole. All the masks inside the house were talking in their animals voices and crying out loud.

All of Wakiash's people awakened. He learned that instead of being gone four days, as he thought, he had been gone four years. The people went into the house with him, and he began to make his dance. He taught the people the songs he had brought back, and while they sang them he danced. When they finished the singing and dancing, the house and the other things went back to the animal people.

Wakiash made a house, masks, and a totem pole of his own from a cedar tree. When he was finished, the people composed a song. It was the first totem pole they had ever had. They named it Kalakuyuwish, which means, "the pole which holds up the sky." They said the reason the totem pole made creaking sounds was because the sky was so heavy. And from that time, Wakiash took the name of the totem pole, Kalakuyuwish. ▫

Questions to Think About

1. What did Wakiash find on his journey?

2. Why do you think a dance of his own was important to Wakiash?

3. Why do you think the animals gave Wakiash what he asked for?

4. What do we have today that is similar to what the totem pole represents?

5. Can you create a dance of your own? What steps would you do?

From Erdoes, Richard and Alfonso Ortiz. *American Indian Myths and Legends,* Pantheon Books, 1984. Originally reported by Natalie Curtis in *The Indian's Book*, 1907.

The Great Canoe in the Sky

Salish

During the time of myth-making, most of the stars were people. At that time, when there were as yet only a few stars in the sky, five Salish Indians lived on the west shore of Flathead Lake. They were very good friends who always worked together. They hunted and fished and went to war together. They were more like brothers than friends.

One summer they looked at the canoes each of them had. They saw that after so many years of use the canoe had become unsafe. The wood was rotting, and two of them had already begun leaking.

One of the friends said to the others, "We must build one canoe for all of us, a large one, so we may continue fishing together. We do not need five separate ones, since we always go together."

Each of the friends agreed to this, and they began to build the new canoe. They planned that when it was finished, they would paddle the canoe across the lake to a shallow bay that they could see. "There are many fish to be caught in that bay," they said to one another. "We will go there together when our canoe is ready."

As they worked and talked, Bluejay listened in on what they were saying. Usually she chattered a great deal, mostly about nothing important. Now, however, as she heard the plans of the five friends, she was very sad. You see,

Bluejay knew that a terrible storm was building. It would arrive at just the time the friends planned to be on the other side of the lake, and they would surely drown.

Bluejay did not know what to do, so she flew to the rocks where Old Man Coyote stood.

"What is troubling you, my little friend?" Old Man Coyote asked. "Why are you so sad?"

"Our five friends are in great danger," she replied. "They are planning to go across the lake at just the time a terrible storm is coming. I do not know what to do. Is there something you can do to help them?"

"I cannot control the water," Old Man Coyote admitted, "but I can do something to keep them from drowning. I will help them go into the Sky World as stars together. There they will be able to work in their canoe together, and the storm will not touch them."

And so that is what he did. He lifted the canoe with the five men in it up into the sky. Now when it is night, we can see them working together just as they did when they were on earth. ⊡

From Clark, Ella E., *Indian Legends of the Pacific Northwest,* University of California Press, 1953.

Questions to Think About

1. Why did the men build one large canoe rather than five small ones?

2. Do you think Bluejay and Old Man Coyote were right to have intervened or should they have let the fishermen take their chances in the storm? Write a new ending for the story in which they don't intervene.

3. What would you have done? How would the story be different?

The Animals Climb into the Sky

Kootenay

The animals once decided to travel to the Sky World. They did not know how to get there until their chief, Grizzly Bear, at last came up with a plan. He called all the animal people together and told them, "Each of you—animal, bird, and fish—will shoot an arrow toward the Sky World until a rope of arrows reaches from this world into the Sky World."

Everyone thought this was a good plan, and they agreed to it. Coyote shot the first arrow, but it fell back down to earth. Fish, Toad, and Snake tried, but their arrows also fell back. One by one the animals tried to hit the Sky, but none succeeded until two Hawks stepped up to take their turns. They had once visited the Sky World and were skillful marksmen, so they felt very confident.

They shot many arrows into the sky, one after the other. The animals could hear the arrows whiz into the air as the second arrow hit the first one in its notch, then the third hit the second, and so on. This continued for a day and a night until the arrows had formed a rope that extended all the way from the ground up into the Sky World. To complete the rope, Raven stuck his bill into the last arrow and braced his feet against the earth to steady it. On this rope the animals climbed from the earth into the sky.

Glutton, who was always mindful of his stomach, said, "I must go check on my traps, first. I will be back shortly," and he left. When he returned, the others had all disappeared up into the sky, leaving him behind. He became very angry and started pulling down all the arrows, throwing them. As he did so, the Rocky Mountains were formed.

Meanwhile, Muskrat, who could be very sneaky, had used his tail to reach the sky ahead of the other animals. With his great power, he made some houses appear in the Sky World. Muskrat then waited for the others to arrive, so he could play a trick on them. When the other animals arrived, Muskrat giggled to himself as he shot at them from the houses. He ran from one place to another, shooting from each place. He wanted the animals to think a lot of people lived there and that the people wanted the animals to leave.

The animals prepared to return to earth, but when they returned to where they had left the rope of arrows, the arrows were gone. They did not know what to do.

Finally the chief said, "We will make a noose and catch Thunderbird. We will put his feathers on ourselves, and they will help us to fly back down to earth."

They waited until they saw a flash of lightning and knew Thunderbird would soon be coming. Then they caught him and pulled out all his feathers. Eagle took the best feathers before he divided up the rest among the other animals. Some animals did not get any, for there were not enough for everyone.

The animals that took feathers flew down from the Sky and became birds. Some animals jumped down to earth and became fish or land animals. Coyote used his tail to steer himself gently down.

The people who did not come back to earth were killed by the Sky People and turned into stars. We can see them twinkling in the Sky every night. ▫

From Clark, Ella Elizabeth, *Indian Legends of Canada*. McClelland and Stewart Ltd., 1992, copyright 1960. Story originally taken from Dr. M. W. Stirling, Director, Bureau of Ethnology, Smithsonian Institution, Washington, D.C.

Questions to Think About

1. *Why do you think the animals wanted to visit the Sky World? What do you suppose they thought they would find?*

2. *Do you think it was right for the animals to go on ahead of Glutton? Why?*

3. *How could the animals have worked together so that everyone could get down from the Sky World?*

The Origin of Cedar Trees

Haida

The Great Creator made the world and placed the Haida people on the beautiful Queen Charlotte Islands where they had peace and much of everything they needed.

One day, however, soon after the people had settled into their new homes, they began to quarrel. They quarreled about almost everything. Finally, the Creator came down from his home in the Sky World and told them, "If you will not learn to live in peace with each other, you will be destroyed."

The Haida were ashamed and sad. They pleaded with the Creator to give them another chance. He agreed to let them try again, and for some time all was well. They were kind and good and stayed together peacefully. But after a time, it all started again. Some people were greedy, wanting their neighbors' things. Some people were jealous and resented the good fortune of another villager. Evil traits spread, and the people forgot they had promised the Creator not to quarrel.

The Creator came again, and this time he said, "You are now going to receive the punishment you have deserved for a long time." With the last sound of his voice, a thick darkness covered the land and did not lift for many days. When it was gone, all the people had changed into cedar trees.

From the sky could be heard the

93

words of the Creator saying, "When new people who can live peacefully together come to these beautiful islands to live, they will use the wood from the red cedar trees for many things. They will build lodges (homes) with planks of the cedar, and with the trunks they will build their canoes. From the roots, the women will weave their baskets and mats, and from the bark, they will weave their clothing. The inner bark they will use for food when it is springtime."

In this way, good came from evil deeds and greed, for the cedar trees gave the Haida people most of the things they needed to live. ▣

From Clark, Ella Elizabeth. *Indian Legends of Canada.* McClelland and Stewart Ltd., 1969.

Questions to Think About

1. Do you think good can come from evil? Can you think of any other stories where it does?

2. Why do you think people seem to find it so hard to live together peacefully?

3. The cedar tree gave the Haida everything they needed to live. Is there another living thing that provided everything they needed to a different group of Native Americans?

The Punishment of the Stingy

Chinook

By the seaside was a big village with many people. Their houses overlooked the sea. There was a pathway that led from the houses to the edge of the water, where canoes were kept.

In this village the Chief died. This Chief had a son who was still a boy, yet nearly a man. It was winter, and food was scarce. The people searched along the sea for something to eat, but they could find little. They began to despair, for even their customary diet of mussels and roots was hard to find. The hunters prepared to go to sea, hoping that if they could find no other food there, they could, at least, find mussels.

Out to sea they went and soon came to a small rock island. Sea lions were on the island. When a hunter speared one, it died and floated to the top of the water. The hunters set about to singe off the sea lion's hair, cut it up, and boil it.

Bluejay, who was one of the hunters, said, "Let us eat it all without taking any of it home to the others."

"I do not think we should do this," said Raven. "I will take some to the hungry people at home," and he put a large piece of the meat into his mat and carried it to the canoe.

Bluejay ran after him and seized the meat. "You must not do that!" he said, and he threw the meat into the fire and burned it up. When the hunters had eaten all they wanted, they gathered up some mussels and left to return home. They arrived at the village, and Bluejay called out, "Wives, come and get your mussels!"

The women hurried to get their mussels and carried them home to cook. Raven gave some to the Chief's son. That night the boy said to Raven, "Tomorrow I want to go with you."

Bluejay said, "You can't do that. The waves will wash you away. I was almost washed away, myself."

Early the next morning the hunters got ready to go back to the island. They boarded their canoes, and as they started to push off, the Chief's son ran to them. "I want to go with you," he said.

Bluejay said to him, "Go home! Go home!" Then he told the hunters, "Hurry up, shove off."

The hunters paddled away and came at last to the island. They went ashore, and one of them speared a sea lion. It died and floated to the surface of the water. They hauled it on shore, and Bluejay said, "We must eat it here or else the Chief's son will always want to come with us."

They singed the animal, cut it up, and boiled it. They cooked the meat and ate their fill. Raven tried to save one piece by tying it in his hair to hide it. Bluejay saw him and ran to him. He took the meat out of Raven's hair, threw it into the fire, and burned it up. When the hunters had eaten all they

wanted, they gathered up some mussels and went home.

When they arrived at the village, Bluejay called out, "Wives, come and get your mussels!" The women hurried down to get their mussels and took them home to cook.

Bluejay told the other hunters, "Do not tell the Chief's son about the sea lion, because if you do, he will want to go with us next time."

That night the boy said to the hunters, "Tomorrow I will go with you."

Bluejay said to him, "You can't go. You might be overwhelmed by the waves and drift away. I almost drifted away today."

The boy said, "I will go with you."

The hunters followed the same routine for two more days with the Chief's son always crying to go with them.

On the fourth morning after first finding the sea lions, the men again prepared to leave. The boy went down to the canoes and tried to climb in. He walked out into the water until he was in up to his armpits, but Bluejay hit his hands and pushed him away. The boy cried as the hunters left.

After the hunters left this time, the boy sadly climbed back up to the village. He got his arrows from the house and walked on the beach until he came to a point where the land jutted out into the water. There he saw a black eagle, which he shot with an arrow. He skinned the eagle and tried to put on the eagle's skin, but it was too small for him. He left the skin there.

He continued to walk until he saw another eagle. He shot the eagle with an arrow and it fell down. He skinned it and tried to put on the skin. It was too small, so he left it there.

He continued walking down the beach until he saw a bald eagle. He shot this one with an arrow. It fell down, and he skinned it and put on the skin. This one was also too small for him, but it was almost big enough. The boy left it on and tried to fly.

At first he could not fly at all. Then he could fly down when he jumped off a cliff, but he could not rise in the air. Finally he was able to rise into the air a little. After trying for a very long time, he learned how to fly well.

He flew back toward the village. On the way he smelled fat cooking, so he turned and flew out to sea, following the smell. He flew over the island where the hunters had gone. He sat on a tree and watched. He could see the hunters cooking fat meat. When they had almost eaten their fill, he flew toward them, thinking to himself, "I wish Bluejay could look up and see me now!"

He flew around them once, then five more times. Bluejay threw a piece of meat at him. The boy-eagle took the piece of meat and flew away.

Bluejay was watching the eagle and said, "Why, that eagle has feet like a boy!"

When the hunters had eaten their fill, Raven again tried unsuccessfully to hide a piece of meat to take home. The hunters gathered some mussels and headed home. When they neared the village, Bluejay called out, "Wives, come get your mussels." The women hurried down to the beach to get their mussels, and then went home to cook them.

Once the boy flew home, he fell asleep. He did not arise the next day until the hunters had already left.

When the Chief's son arose, he called together all the women and children. "Hurry!" he said to them. "Wash yourselves and comb your hair." They did as he said.

Then the Chief's son put a plank of wood on the ground with the meat he had brought from the island the day before. He said, "Your husbands eat much of this meat every day." He used the fat meat to grease the heads of all the women and children. He pulled out of the ground all the planks of which the houses were made and sharpened the ends of them. Raven lived at the end of the village, but the Chief's son did not pull up the planks of his house.

The Chief's son fastened the planks on the backs of the women and children. Then he said, "Go to the beach and into the sea. Find the rock island that is out there and swim around it five times. After you do this, swim out to sea, for from now on you will be killer whales. When you find sea lions, you should always kill them, but do not give any of the meat to stingy people. When you kill a whale, eat it, but do not give any to stingy people. I will take these children with me. They will live on the sea and be my relations."

He next split sinews and threw them down on the stones where the people used to get mussels. He said to the mussels, "When Bluejay and those others try to take you from the rocks, you must always stick tight to the rocks."

The women went into the sea and began to swim. Soon they were jumping out of the water. They swam five times in front of the village, then headed seaward.

Bluejay saw them coming and said, "What is this coming toward us?"

The women swam around the island five times, jumping out of the water all the while; then they headed out to sea. Birds with bills red as blood flew after them.

Bluejay saw them and said, "Where are those birds coming from?"

Raven answered, "Do you not recognize your own children?" The birds flew around the island five times, then they flew away to sea.

The hunters were eating the meat they had killed, and they became very uneasy. "Let us go home," one said. "I am afraid we have seen bad spirits."

They gathered some mussels and put the meat they had left into the canoes and started for home. As they neared the village, Bluejay called out, "Wives, come and get your mussels."

No one answered. They went up on the beach, and no one was there. Their homes were gone, as well. Only Raven's house still stood.

After that, when Raven walked along the beach, he sometimes found a sturgeon or other fish, and once he found a porpoise. When Bluejay walked along the beach, however, he never found anything. When he tried to gather mussels, he could not pull them off, for they were stuck tightly to the rocks. He often cried because he was always hungry.

The men who had taken nothing home to their wives and children now found their homes and families gone. They now had nothing except roots to eat. Their Chief had punished them for being stingy. ⊡

From Grinnell, George Bird. *The Punishment of the Stingy*. University of Nebraska Press, Lincoln and London, 1982. Reprinted from the original published by Harper & Brothers, 1901.

Questions to Think About

1. Why did Bluejay not want to share the sea lion meat with the rest of the village?

2. Why do you think Raven did not just tell the others about the sea lions when he got home?

3. What would you have done if you were one of the hunters?

ANSWER KEY

STORIES FROM THE EASTERN WOODLANDS

GREAT TURTLE MAKES THE WORLD

1. They did not think a small animal could succeed in such a great task when larger animals had failed.
2. Possible answers include: the challenge to be the one to succeed, the need to please Great Turtle, the desire to provide soil for First Lady to live on.
3. Great Turtle was the head animal.

THE BROKEN WING

1. They were family and loved each other.
2. Discuss all reasonable responses.

LONE BIRD, THE WOMAN IN THE MOON

1. She did not want to leave her parents with whom she was happy.
2. She was afraid of being alone.
3. Discuss all reasonable responses.
4. Perhaps he felt it was all right as long as she was happy.
5. Possible answers include: Yes, because she was no longer alone; No, because she was no longer with her family. Discuss all reasonable answers.

LITTLE PEOPLE OF THE MICMAC

1. Her parents told her to return him.
2. This is a good opportunity to discuss how children should behave with strangers and any offers they might make.
3. Discuss how people's perspectives of an event can vary.

THE ORIGIN OF CORN

1. He promised anything just so she would stay with him.
2. She may have loved him, and she wanted him to always have food.
3. Point out that these are legends, and legends

would not be what they are if they did not have some drama in them.
4. Student answers will vary.

ORIGIN OF THE PLEIADES

1. They were mad at their mothers.
2. Children today still do things to spite their parents.
3. It explains the constellation Pleiades, or Anit' sutsa
4. The mothers probably suffered more although it is hard to give a definite answer.
5. This is hard to answer, but accept all reasonable explanations.

HOW DEER GOT HIS HORNS

1. The winner was to receive antlers.
2. Possible answers: Yes, because Deer was familiar with the area; No, because it gave him an unfair advantage.
3. The lesson is not to cheat, cheaters never win, or any other such lesson.
4. No, because they showed the cheater losing not winning.
5. Perhaps; he did not win by cheating.

STORIES FROM THE GREAT PLAINS

OLD MAN TEACHES THE PEOPLE

1. He created the world and the people.
2. He taught them to make arrows so they could hunt buffalo.
3. The Native Americans believed this was their land, given to them by the spirits. This is their way of justifying why European settlers had no right to it.
4. Probably, since they no longer control the land.
5. Possible answer: This legend seems more realistic because one spirit created everything as opposed to animals and magical powers as in *Great Turtle Makes the World*.

WHITE BUFFALO WOMAN

1. He was unworthy of being near the woman since he had bad thoughts about her.
2. The Native Americans had great respect for the earth and sky so it would be natural for these things to be on a sacred pipe.
3. They believe only good can come from the pipe.
4. The woman was probably a spirit because she was able to turn into a buffalo.

THE BOY AND THE TURTLES

1. He was hunting for turtles.
2. The turtles turned into Little Men.
3. He was unable to talk and was beating his sides.
4. It was believed that the first one to see the Little People must be someone who is holy and special even if he or she runs.

STORIES FROM THE SOUTHWEST

COYOTE AND THE WOODPECKERS

1. He was jealous because Woodpecker and his family had pretty colors under their wings.
2. Father Coyote was in the wrong because he was more worried about being embarrassed than caring about his children's safety.
3. Don't try to be something you are not; don't put on airs to impress people.
4. Discuss all reasonable responses.

THE MOTHER MOON

1. The people and animals needed time to rest.
2. She felt his light was more important than hers.
3. Discuss all reasonable responses.
4. No. Nighttime would be brighter than daytime.

TURKEY MAKES CORN AND COYOTE PLANTS IT

1. They got the seeds from Turkey.
2. They believed he was stealing from them.
3. Discuss both sides of this issue.
4. Those who work hard are rewarded; it is better to learn to provide for yourself rather than always having others provide for you.

THE COYOTE AND THE BEAR

1. Bear always outsmarts Coyote and caused Coyote to get stuck in the ice and then did nothing to help him.
2. He did not think things through.
3. Possible answers include: not to trust Bear; to think things out.
4. Probably not if he learned his lesson. Discuss students' opinions.

STORIES FROM THE FAR WEST

THE ORIGIN OF THE SIERRA NEVADA AND THE COAST RANGE

1. Hawk and Crow built them up out of mud from Duck's beak. Hawk built one mountain range and Crow built the other. But Hawk switched the mountains around when he saw that Crow built his mountains higher than Hawk's.
2. Crow wanted to trick Hawk so he made his mountains higher.
3. Possible answers include: for fun, to trick Hawk, to show he could do something better than Hawk, and so on.
4. He didn't seem to mind because he did nothing about it.

COYOTE MAKES FIRST MAN

1. Coyote created Man.
2. They were vain.
3. Answers will vary. Discuss all reasonable answers.

HOW ROBIN GOT HIS RED BREAST

1. To keep the fire from going out, Robin protected it with his body thus burning his breast.
2. Yes. You can make a fire by rubbing two sticks together and Robin does have a red breast.

Stories from the Northwest

PUSHING UP THE SKY

1. All of the people spoke different languages.
2. It showed how people could work together to achieve a common goal; animals and people became stars.
3. We can accomplish great things when we work together.

WAKIASH AND THE FIRST TOTEM POLE

1. He found a dance of his own, songs, and a totem pole.
2. He wanted to have something that all of the other Chiefs had.
3. Possible answers include: they may have been afraid of him; they were ashamed to be seen as people and hoped he would not tell anyone if they gave him what he wished; he arrived on a raven; they wanted to.
4. Some people have a family crest and many Native Americans of the Northwest still have totem poles.
5. Answers will vary.

THE GREAT CANOE IN THE SKY

1. They did not need five individual canoes since they always fished together.
2. Discuss all reasonable answers but be sure to touch on the idea that they might not have drowned or that they would not like to be stars.
3. Answers will vary.

THE ANIMALS CLIMB INTO THE SKY

1. Possible answers include: they were curious and thought they might find something of value.
2. Discuss how it is not nice to leave without others, but it is also not nice to keep your friends waiting while you eat.
3. Discuss various solutions such as having those with wings helping down those who do not have wings or perhaps building some sort of primitive flying machine with the wings. Let the children use their imaginations to answer this one.

THE ORIGIN OF CEDAR TREES

1. Answers will vary.
2. Answers will vary.
3. The buffalo.

THE PUNISHMENT OF THE STINGY

1. He was greedy.
2. Maybe he was afraid of Bluejay and the other hunters, or maybe he did not think the others would believe him without any proof.
3. Answers will vary. Discuss all appropriate responses.

NOTES